TANKS

★ AND ARMORED FIGHTING VEHICLES ★

TANKS

★ AND ARMORED FIGHTING VEHICLES ★

ROBERT JACKSON

Bath · New York · Singapore · Hong Kong · Cologne · Delhi · Melbourne

First published by Parragon in 2008
Parragon
Queen Street House
4 Queen Street
Bath BA1 1HE, UK

Copyright © Parragon Books Ltd 2008

ISBN 978-1-4075-2429-0

Editorial and design by
Amber Books Ltd
Bradley's Close
74–77 White Lion Street
London N1 9PF
www.amberbooks.co.uk

Project Editor: Sarah Uttridge
Design: Graham Curd
Picture Research: Kate Green and Terry Forshaw

Printed in China

Picture Credits
All © Art-Tech/Aerospace except the following:
Alcaniz Freson's S.A: 9 (t), 11 (b), 12 (b), 13 (b), 14, 17, 18 (b), 20 (b), 36/37, 44 (b)
Amber Books: 10 (b), 21 (b), 22, 24 (t), 26, 28 (b), 30/31, 40, 41 (b), 48 (b), 50 (t),
54/55, 61 (b), 62/63, 66/67, 74/75, 78 (b), 79, 80 (b), 82 (b)
Art-Tech/MARS: 36 (t), 53 (both)
BAE Systems: 6 (t), 71 (both). 84/85, 85
Corbis: 43 (t)
Christopher Foss: 86, 89, 90
Rheinmetall Landsysteme GmbH: 93 (both)
Richard Stickland: 29 (t)
Cody Images: 5 (cl), 5 (r), 7, 8 (b), 10 (t), 11 (t), 13 (t), 16, 18 (t), 20 (t), 25 (b),
27 (t), 28 (t), 35 (both), 39 (b), 41 (t), 44 (t), 45 (t), 46 (t), 48 (t), 49 (both), 52 (b),
55, 57, 59 (t), 60 (b), 64 (t), 65, 68, 69, 73 (b), 78 (t), 82 (t), 87 (b)
U.S. Department of Defense/U.S. Army: 5 (cr), 72, 75 (b), 87 (t)

CONTENTS

INTRODUCTION

This fascinating book tells the story of the tank, from its first use to

break the stalemate of trench warfare in World War I, to the present day.

The first attack by British Mk I tanks took place on 15 September 1916 and met with only limited success. On 20 November 1917, the British launched the first tank offensive in history, when 476 tanks forced a 12-mile (19km) breach in the strongest sector of the Hindenburg Line at Cambrai. Whereas the Germans remained deficient in armor—they never produced more than 13 tanks in any one battle—the British had a total of 1184 tanks on the Western Front by July 1918. The first ever tank-versus-tank engagement took place on 24 April 1918, when three British Mk IVs engaged three German

Below: *A large proportion of Soviet armored strength in the 1950s and 1960s was provided by the T-54 and T-55 series of MBTs. They are the most widely produced tank in history.*

Above: *Armed with a 2.95in (75mm) main gun, the M24 Chaffee light tank was introduced into service in 1944. In the postwar years it was used as the basis for a new family of fighting vehicles.*

heavy A7Vs. One of the latter was knocked out, although not before the Germans had disabled three lightly armored Whippet tanks that had been shooting up infantry.

The lessons of World War I were not lost on Germany's military leaders under the Nazi regime. Under the guidance of General Hans Seekt, they developed the tank as an instrument of mobile warfare and formulated the classic Blitzkrieg (Lightning War) tactics in which their Panzer divisions, preceded by ground attack aircraft like the Junkers Ju 87 Stuka dive-bomber, plunged deep into enemy territory and created corridors that were then exploited by mechanised infantry.

Such tactics worked well in the Battle of France and in North Africa, although in the latter case the Germans were ultimately foiled by Allied air supremacy. The tactics also worked well in the early phase of the attack on Russia, but received a shock in the form of Russia's heavily-armed KV-1 and T-34 tanks, whose 3.0in (76mm) guns could penetrate the Wehrmacht tanks' armor while remaining immune to German anti-tank munitions.

To meet this new challenge, the Germans launched a crash industrial programme to build a new generation of massive, heavily armored fighting vehicles. Two of its products were the Tiger and the Panther. The

43-ton (43,690kg) Panther tank, with frontal armor of 3.2in (83mm) thickness, a speed of 28mph (45km/h) and a main armament of one 3.0in (75mm) gun was, without doubt, the best tank produced by any side during World War II, and elements of its design were reflected in post-war armored fighting vehicles like the British Centurion.

The 49-ton (49,786kg) Centurion Mk 3 of the late 1950s, with an electronically-stabilised 3.28in (83.4mm), and later 4.1in (105mm) gun, was an outstanding example. When it began to be phased out of British service in 1960, other nations were keen to acquire it. So good a design was the Centurion that it continued to serve in some numbers into the 1990s. Together with the American M48, it wrought havoc on Egypt's Russian-built tanks in the 1967 Arab-Israeli war.

These two machines were the progenitors of a line of armored fighting vehicles which culminated in two excellent designs that saw action in Iraq in the Gulf War of 1991 and again in 2003. Capable of taking on the latest Russian-designed equipment and destroying it with almost ridiculous ease, America's M1 Abrams and Britain's Challenger will certainly rank alongside the Panther as the most effective tanks ever built.

⚒ 1916 UK

MARK I MEDIUM TANK

It was Britain's tanks that finally broke the stalemate on the Western Front in World War I, overcoming the enemy's trench systems. The first of these was the Mk I—noisy, smelly, and prone to breaking down.

Above: The Mk I was fitted with an antigrenade mesh on top of the hull, as seen in this photograph.

Specifications

Armament: Two 6pdr (2.25in/57mm) guns; one Hotchkiss 0.303in (7.7mm) MG

Armor: 0.23–0.47in (6–12mm)

Crew: 8

Dimensions: Length 32ft 6in (9.7m); Width 13ft 9in (4.12m); Height 7ft 11in (2.41m)

Weight: 28 tons (28,450kg)

Powerplant: Daimler 6-cylinder gasoline developing 150bhp (111.8kW) at 1000rpm

Speed: 3.7mph (5.95km/h)

Range: 22 miles (37.8km)

The British Mk I tank of 1916, known first as Centipede, then as Big Willie, and finally as Mother, was born out of a need for a tracked fighting vehicle that was capable of crossing a 12ft (3.5m) trench. The design that evolved was unlike anything seen before. The rhomboidal-shaped vehicle had tracks carried right around the hull, and a sponson on each side to house 2.25in (57mm) guns or machine guns. Mother was tested for the first time on January 16, 1916, and successful trials were completed within three weeks. Orders for 100 examples of the tank, now called Mk I, were placed in February, and training of the first crews began.

Above: Originally, the Mk I tank was fitted with a wheel at the stern for steering purposes. This was found to be quite ineffective and was soon discarded, applying brakes to the tracks proving a better option.

Insight into the future

The Mk I first went into action on September 15, 1916, when 32 vehicles were employed along a five-mile front. They were successful, especially when several tanks operated together. A few days later, a single British tank moved ahead of the infantry and cooperated with a low-flying aircraft to capture an enemy trench. This was a dramatic pointer to the future.

1917 France

RENAULT FT-17 LIGHT TANK

Arguably the finest tank of its era, the Renault FT-17 Light continued in service for many years after World War I. Some countries were still using it as a frontline tank in 1939.

Specifications

Armament: One 1.46in (37mm) gun; one or two machine guns
Armor: 0.47in (12mm)
Crew: 2
Dimensions: Length (with tail) 16ft 5in (5m); Width 5 ft 7in (1.71m); Height 7ft (2.13m)
Weight: 6.485 tons (6589kg)
Powerplant: One Renault liquid-cooled four-cylinder gasoline engine developing 35hp (26kW)
Speed: 4.8mph (7.7 km/h)
Range: 22 miles (35.4km)

Above: *The Renault FT-17 infantry support tank was one of the most successful of the early armored fighting vehicles, although it was difficult to maintain. Thousands were produced.*

The French FT-17 light tank was designed in 1917 and had a huge impact on future tank design. It featured a rotating turret mounted on top of the hull, and also had a rear-mounted engine. Because of the French War Department's enthusiasm for super-heavy tanks, the FT-17 might never have been produced had it not been for the enthusiasm and continuing support of Colonel Jean-Baptiste Eugène Estienne. He persuaded key figures in the French military that a light infantry support tank would be a valuable tool. The first FT-17s were deployed in March 1917 and were first used in action in May 1918. In July of that year, enough of these tanks were available that 480 were concentrated for a successful French counterattack near Soissons. The FT-17 was also used by the American Expeditionary Force in France from the summer of 1918. The type continued to serve in substantial numbers for years after World War I. Several variants, such as command vehicles, were produced. As Renault did not have the capacity to produce the large numbers of FT-17s on order, production was allocated to various subsidiary manufacturers.

Below: *This example of an FT-17 features a cast, rather than a riveted turret. The original FT-17 was not used in action until May 1918, but after a slow start large numbers were deployed.*

⚒ **1917 Germany**

A7V STURMPANZERWAGEN

The A7V Sturmpanzerwagen was Germany's first viable tank, and was successfully used in the Ludendorff Offensive of March 1918. It fought the first-ever tank-versus-tank battle.

Above: The A7V was armed with up to seven machine guns, which meant that it had to carry a large crew. The interior was consequently cramped and uncomfortable, with available space strictly limited.

Specifications

Armament: One 2.24in (57mm) gun; six or seven 0.312in (7.92mm) MGs

Armor: Maximum, 1.18in (30mm)

Crew: Up to 18

Dimensions: Length, overall, 26ft 3in (8m); Width 10ft (3.05m); Height 10ft 10in (3.3m)

Weight: approx 30 tons (30,480kg)

Powerplant: Two Daimler-Benz, 4-cylinder gasoline, each delivering 100hp (74.5kW)

Speed: Road, 8mph (12.8km/h)

Range: Road, 25 miles (40.2km)

Developing armored fighting vehicles had a much lower priority for the Germans than for the British and French during World War I. By 1917 the Germans were on the defensive, and it was argued that tanks, as offensive weapons, had no place in defensive strategy. Nor did they have a part to play in the war on the Eastern Front, as the Russian armies were on the verge of collapse. The A7V Committee was formed in October 1917 to study the concept of the armored fighting vehicle. By the end of the year this committee had designed a machine based on the Holt suspension. A year passed before an order was placed for 100 examples of a 30 ton (30,480kg) fighting vehicle—the A7V Sturmpanzerwagen.

Above: The A7V was Germany's first successful tank design, and was used to good effect during the Ludendorff Offensive of March 1918. It took part in the world's first tank-versus-tank battle.

Ludendorff Offensive

The Germans only ever managed to produce 20 A7Vs, relying on captured German and French AFVs to bolster their armored force. Despite this, four A7Vs—together with five captured British Mk IVs—played a vital part during the Ludendorff Offensive of March 21, 1918. They advanced in the wake of a five-hour artillery barrage and punched a five-mile hole through the British defenses at St. Quentin.

⚒ **1935 France**

SOMUA S-35 MEDIUM TANK

The SOMUA S-35 was well-protected and agile, and was the finest tank in the world in 1940, incorporating many novel features that had escaped the attention of other designers.

Left: *The SOMUA medium tank was an excellent design, but its development was plagued by industrial disputes and successive changes of government. It never reached France's frontline armored units in sufficient numbers.*

Specifications

Armament: One 1.85in (47mm) gun; one 0.295in (7.5mm) MG

Armor: Maximum, 1.57in (40mm)

Crew: 3

Dimensions: Length 17ft 7.8in (5.38m); Width 6ft 11in (2.12m); Height 8ft 7in (2.62m)

Weight: 19.2 tons (19,500kg)

Powerplant: SOMUA V-8 gasoline, 190hp (141.7kW)

Speed: Road, 25.3mph (40.7km/h)

Range: Road, 143 miles (230km)

The SOMUA (Société d'Outillage Mécanique et d'Usinage d'Artillerie) was designed in response to a requirement for a new cavalry tank issued in 1934. Two prototypes were built, and an order for an initial batch of 50 tanks was placed in 1935. The official designation of the tank was the Automitrailleuse de Combat Modèle 1935S, although in practice it was commonly known as the SOMUA S-35. A fast, hard-hitting tank, with an excellent 1.85in (47mm) main armament, the SOMUA had one major drawback: Its commander was also the gunner, and was expected to direct the tank at the same time as loading, training, and firing the main gun. The turret itself was a version of the APX-1, also used in the Char B1. This tank's experience of real combat revealed a design defect: The upper and lower halves of the hull were joined by a horizontal ring of bolts, and if this joint line was hit by an antitank projectile, the vehicle split in two.

Innovations

The SOMUA's innovations included self-sealing fuel tanks on either side of the rear-mounted engine. Each tank was equipped to carry a radio transceiver, but a shortage of the required ER28 sets meant that only the commander's tank in a platoon of five vehicles was radio-equipped. Throughout the period of its production, the SOMUA was plagued by industrial disputes and other labor problems. It consequently entered service at a much slower rate than had been planned.

In action, the SOMUA could outpace and outgun the German Panzer III, but the German tank was much more reliable mechanically. The SOMUA experienced problems with its complex suspension. Despite its problems, the SOMUA acquitted itself well during the Battle of France. In battle, the SOMUA battalions suffered more from dive-bomber attacks than they did from enemy tank engagements.

Below: *If the SOMUA had a design fault, it was its high profile, which made it an easy target. The commander also had to act as the gunner, which made it difficult for him to exercise control in combat.*

1935 Germany

PANZERKAMPFWAGEN II

Above: *A Panzer II (right) in France during the German invasion of May 1940. The Panzer II played a key part in ensuring the rapid German victory. The other tank in the picture is a Panzer 38 (t).*

The Panzer II bridged the gap between the Panzer I and later, much more viable armored fighting vehicles. Crews used it to practice the tactics that could take the future Panzer divisions to early victory in World War II.

The PzKpfw II was in the nature of an interim light tank, ordered in 1934 to bridge the gap between the Panzer I and the new generation of AFVs, the PzKpfw III and PzKpfw IV. The specification called for a 10-ton armored vehicle mounting a 0.79in (20mm) gun in a fully revolving turret. Henschel, Krupp, and MAN of Augsburg all responded; Krupp's proposal was the simplest, involving the mounting of a 0.79in (20mm) cannon and machine gun in the existing PzKpfw I, but it was the vehicle developed by MAN that was selected for production.

Industrial tractor

The firm produced several prototypes under the cover-name Landwirtschaftlicher Schlepper (industrial tractor), and the vehicle was accepted for production. MAN was responsible for the chassis and Daimler-Benz for the superstructure. The first production PzKpfw Ausführung A tanks were delivered in 1935 and production continued well into 1942, despite the experience of the French campaign of 1940 showing that the vehicle was obsolete. Several variants were produced, one of the most interesting being an amphibious version intended for the invasion of England in 1940.

Specifications

(PzKpfw II Ausführung F)

Armament: One 0.79in (20mm) cannon; one 0.315in (7.92mm) MG

Armor: Maximum, 1.38in (35mm)

Crew: 3

Dimensions: Length 15ft 9.4in (4.81m); Width 7ft 5.75in (2.28m); Height 7ft 0.6in (2.15m)

Weight: Approx 9.5 tons (9650kg)

Powerplant: Maybach HL62TR, 6-cylinder gasoline, 140hp (104.4kW)

Speed: Road, 24.85mph (40km/h)

Range: Road, 124 miles (200km)

Below: *The Panzerkampfwagen II was intended as an interim design pending the introduction of more effective AFVs like the Panzer III, but it continued in production for a long time and saw much action in World War II.*

PANZERKAMPFWAGEN III MEDIUM TANK

The Panzer III was produced in large numbers, and when Germany invaded the Soviet Union in 1941, it was the most widely produced German tank. Many of these tanks were later adapted as self-propelled guns.

Above: A Panzer III fording a river. The Mk III was instrumental in Rommel's early victories over the British Commonwealth forces in North Africa, being able to out-fight every type of British tank.

Left: The Panzer III was without doubt one of the best tanks to be produced during World War II, with several versions used for different tasks. It was originally designed as a tank destroyer.

Specifications

(Panzer III Ausführung F)
Armament: One 1.46in (37mm) gun; two 0.312in (7.92mm) MGs
Armor: Maximum, 1.18in (30mm)
Crew: 5
Dimensions: Length 17ft 4.5in (5.38m); Width 9ft 10.9in (2.91m); Height 7ft 11.75in (2.435m)
Weight: approx 19.2 tons (19,500kg)
Powerplant: Maybach HL120 TRM, V-12 gasoline, 300hp (223.7kW)
Speed: Road, 24.8mph (40km/h)
Range: Road, 102.5 miles (165km)

In the mid-1930s, the German Army decreed that each armored battalion should be equipped with three companies of relatively light medium tanks and one company of heavier and more powerful support tanks (the latter emerging as the Panzer Mk IV). The Panzer III medium tank was designed as a result of this. While the Panzer IV was designed for the infantry support role, the Panzer III was intended to fight and destroy other tanks. Mass production of the tank began in 1939.

Models A–G

The first three production models (Ausführungen A, B and C) were built in relatively small numbers, and were used during the invasion of Poland in September 1939. The next model (D) had thicker armor and a revised cupola, and in 1940 Ausführung F entered production. This last model was armed with a high-velocity 1.97in (50mm) gun and an uprated engine, and was fitted with only six roadwheels. The Ausführung G had a similar armament, but featured a still-more powerful engine. By mid-1941 the Panzer III was the most popular German tank, and most machines had been retro-fitted with the 1.97in (50mm) gun. It was used successfully against the British Army in North Africa in late 1941, when every type of British tank was outgunned.

⚒ **1937 Germany**

PANZERKAMPFWAGEN IV MEDIUM TANK

The Panzer IV was one of the most famous tanks ever produced and became the workhorse of the German Panzer divisions in World War II, operating in many different roles.

Below: This Panzer IVG, depicted late in the war, has had extra armor plate added to its hull and turret to protect it against the latest Allied antitank projectiles. It was still a match for tanks such as the Sherman.

One of the most important armored fighting vehicles of World War II, the Panzer IV was intended for the infantry support role, leaving the Panzer III to deal with enemy armor. Krupp was the manufacturer, and the first Panzer IV came off the assembly line in October 1937. The driving force behind the development of Germany's new medium tanks—restricted to these two types by economic constraints—was Colonel Heinz Guderian. His plan was to concentrate these armored fighting vehicles in formations—the celebrated Panzer divisions—instead of splitting them up in packages between the field armies. It was a formula that worked with devastating effect.

Firing problems

The Panzer IV was armed with the short 2.95in (75mm) KwK L/24 low-velocity gun. This fired a high-explosive round and was effective against fortifications and infantry, but it lacked accuracy. In 1941, after the first encounters between the Panzer IV and the Russian T-34, the Panzer IV Ausführung F was equipped with a redesigned turret mounting a more powerful 2.95in (75mm) L/43 antitank gun. In this guise, it became the Panzer IVF2, later renamed the Panzer IVG. This variant became the workhorse of the German armored divisions and remained unchanged except for upgrades to its main armament and armor, as dictated by operational experience. These upgrades, particularly in guns and sighting systems, enabled the Panzer IV to hold its own with the Russian T-34 and the American Sherman, which it encountered for the first time in North Africa in 1942.

Specifications

(PzKpfw IV Ausführung F2)
Armament: One 2.95in (75mm) gun; two 0.312in (7.92mm) MGs
Armor: Maximum, 1.97in (50mm)
Crew: 5
Dimensions: Length 21ft 9in (6.63m); Width 9ft 5.5in (2.88m); Height 8ft 9.5in (2.68m)
Weight: approx 22 tons (22,350kg)
Powerplant: Maybach HL120 TRM, V-12 gasoline, 300hp (223.7kW)
Speed: Road, 24.8mph (40km/h)
Range: Road, 130 miles (209km)

Above: *Panzer IVs advancing across the Russian steppes in 1943. These tanks have been upgraded to carry a 2.95in (75mm) long-barrel high-velocity gun, but they lack the extra armor that would be a later feature.*

Successful operations

The Panzer IV remained in production throughout World War II, some machines being supplied to Germany's satellites. About 40 were converted to amphibious tanks, originally for the projected invasion of England, and were used in the invasion of the Soviet Union. Others, fitted with additional radio equipment, were used as command vehicles. The last variant was the Ausführung J, which appeared in March 1944. In all, production amounted to some 9000 vehicles. Many Panzer IV chassis were converted to specialized roles such as tank destroyers, self-propelled howitzers, and recovery vehicles. The Panzer IV continued to be used after 1945, notably in Syria, which purchased a number of these machines. They were then used to shell Israeli settlements from positions on the Golan Heights during the brief so-called "Water War" conflict of 1965. The surviving Panzer IVs were captured by Israel during the Six-Day War of 1967, to become museum pieces.

Below: *The Ausführung A was one of the earliest models of the Panzer IV. The turret design was substantially modified at a later date and most of the "A" models were used for training.*

1937 Japan

TYPE 97 TE-KE TANKETTE

The small Type 97 Te-Ke Tankette was used in China and the Pacific during World War II, and provided infantry support as well as reconnaissance.

Specifications

Armament: One 1.46in (37mm) gun
Armor: 0.63in (16mm)
Crew: 2
Dimensions: Length 12ft 1in (3.68m); Width 5ft 11in (1.80m); Height 5ft 10in (1.77m)
Weight: 4.67 tons (4750kg)
Powerplant: Ikega 4-cylinder diesel, 65bhp (48.5kW)
Speed: 26mph (42km/h)
Range: 155 miles (250km)

Two prototypes of the Type 97 Te-Ke Tankette were produced by Tokyo Motor Industries in 1937 in response to an Imperial Japanese Army requirement for a small armored reconnaissance vehicle. The original model had the engine and driver at the front and the small turret at the rear, but this was later moved forward to allow better crew communication. The engine then moved to the back. As was common with small and cramped reconnaissance vehicles, the interior was lined with asbestos to give the crew some protection from the heat. The hull was riveted and the driver sat on the left of the commander, who gained access to the turret via a hinged hatch at the rear.

Infantry support

The Type 97 Te-Ke was used on all fronts, but its principal application was in China, where it was sometimes used for infantry support. It could also be used to tow an ammunition trailer. Generally, the Type 97 Te-Ke was organized in companies of up to 17 vehicles. Some of these were salvaged from Pacific islands many years after World War II and have been restored for museum display.

Below: *The Type 97 Te-Ke could hardly be called a success. Its gun was completely ineffective against all types of Allied armor, while its own riveted hull could be penetrated by small-arms fire.*

1938 Czechoslovakia

LT-38 MEDIUM TANK

The LT-38 was another example of the excellence of the tanks designed in Czechoslovakia before World War II. It was widely used by Germany's allies on the Eastern Front from 1941 onward.

Below: The LT-38 was a modified version of the Czech LT-H, produced for Germany and her allies. It saw considerable service with Germany's "satellite" countries, Hungary, Slovakia, Romania, and Bulgaria.

The LT-38 medium tank, built in Czechoslovakia, was used by the German Army under the name of Panzerkampfwagen 38(t). It was designed in 1937 in response to an urgent requirement from the Czech Army for a new light tank, in the light of the rapidly deteriorating international situation. The LT-38 was a conventional pre-World War II tank design, with riveted armor and rear-mounted engine. The centrally located two-man turret housed the main armament, a Skoda A7 gun and a 0.312in (7.92mm) machine gun. A second machine gun of similar caliber, manned by the radio operator, was mounted

in the forward hull next to the driver. The tank was an instant export success, 50 vehicles being purchased by Iran and 24 by Peru and Switzerland respectively. The Czech Army also ordered 150, but none had entered service before Czechoslovakia was overrun by the Germans in 1939.

Production of the LT-38 continued after the German occupation and the tank was used by the Wehrmacht and Germany's satellites—Hungary, Slovakia, Romania, and Bulgaria. The LT-38 chassis also served as the basis for assault guns, antiaircraft guns and antitank guns.

Specifications

Armament: One 1.46in (37mm) cannon (or 37mm KwK L/40 or L/45); two 0.312in (7.92mm) MGs

Armor: 0/59–0.98in (15–25mm)

Crew: 4

Dimensions: Length 15ft 1in (4.60m); Width 6ft 11in (2.12m); Height 7ft 10in (2.4m)

Weight: 9.25 tons (9400kg)

Powerplant: Praga EPA model I 6-cylinder gasoline, 125bhp (93kW) at 2000rpm

Speed: 26mph (42km/h)

Range: 155 miles (250km)

✖ 1938 UK

MATILDA II INFANTRY

The Matilda II took the Germans by surprise during the fighting in France in 1940. Too few of them were available to have an appreciable effect on the campaign, however.

Specifications

Armament: One 2pdr (1.57in/40mm) gun; one 0.31in (7.92mm) Besa MG

Armor: 0.51–3.07in (13–78mm)

Crew: 4

Dimensions: Length 18ft 5in (5.613m); Width 8ft 6in (2.59m); Height 8ft 3in (2.515m)

Weight: 26.5 tons (26,925kg)

Powerplant: Two gasoline 6-cylinder AEC engines, 87bhp (64.8kW)

Speed: 15mph (24km/h)

Range: 160 miles (257km)

Below: *The Matilda II was the only British tank with enough armor to withstand German antitank projectiles in the early years of World War II. After its brief moment of glory at Arras in May 1940, it fought in the Western Desert. The pictured tank is a German operated version.*

Above: *A Matilda II being unloaded at a port on the Suez Canal. The Matilda served the British 8th Army well, but was armed only with the two-pounder gun, which had no effect on enemy tanks like the Panzer Mk III.*

Properly called the Tank, Infantry, Mk II, but more widely known as the Matilda II to distinguish it from the earlier (and unrelated) Matilda I, this was the best British tank in service at the outset of World War II. It was designed at the Royal Arsenal, Woolwich, built by the Vulcan Foundry, and finally produced in 1937, but only two were in service at the outbreak of war in September 1939. Over the next four years, some 2987 Matildas were built until production ceased in August 1943. Because of the thickness of its armor, the Matilda proved virtually immune to the fire of the German tanks encountered in France. In one memorable action at Arras on May 21, 1940, 16 Matildas, backed up by 58 of the smaller Mk Is (armed with machine guns) severely disrupted the advance of General Erwin Rommel's 7th Panzer Division. The British attack was only halted when the Matildas came up against 3.46in (88mm) antiaircraft guns, hastily turned into antitank weapons on Rommel's orders.

British-design success

Over 1000 Matildas were sent to the Soviet Union and were used from the winter of 1941. Others were used by the 4th Australian Armoured Brigade in New Guinea and Borneo until the end of hostilities. The Matilda was therefore the only British-designed tank in service from the start to the end of World War II.

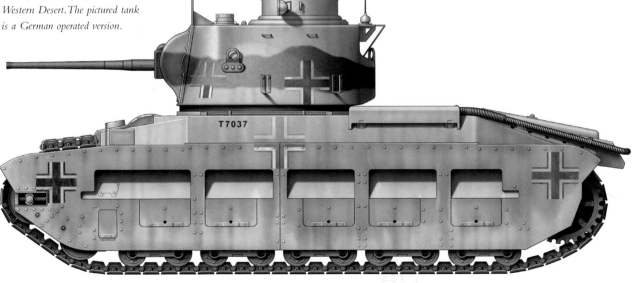

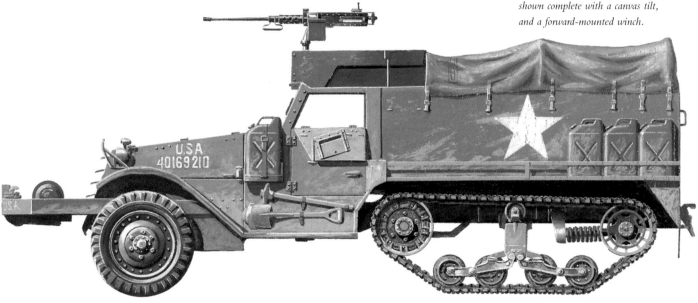

✂ 1938 USA

M3 HALFTRACK

The M3 Halftrack was perhaps the most widely recognized vehicle in World War II, and appeared in every theater of war.

Below: The M3 was the most widely used Allied halftrack of World War II, serving with all the Allied forces. This example is shown complete with a canvas tilt, and a forward-mounted winch.

Widely used by the American and other Allied forces during World War II, the M3 Halftrack became a familiar sight, including an appearance on the Russian Front. In the 1920s, the American Army

Below: This photograph shows the M3's forward-mounted winch and the "pulpit" machine-gun mounting. The vehicle is armed with a 0.5in (12.7mm) Browning heavy machine gun.

purchased some Citroen Kegresse P17 halftracks, and was sufficiently impressed by their performance to order the development of a US vehicle, which emerged in prototype form as the T14 in 1931. Known as the M2 in US Army service, the halftrack formed the hull of a White M2 scout car with a Kegresse halftrack suspension. Four US manufacturers were involved in producing the halftracks, turning out 41,000 between 1941 (when the M2 entered production) and 1944.

M3 variants

Later, the M2 was supplemented by the Half-Track Personnel Carrier M3, which could also be used as a communications vehicle, an artillery towing vehicle and an armored ambulance. One of the disadvantages of the M3 was its lack of floor armor, making its passengers vulnerable to mines. M2 and M3 Halftracks were used by the US forces in the Korean War, by the French in Indo-China and by the Israelis in their early postwar conflicts.

Specifications

(M3A2)

Armament: One 0.50in (12.7mm) MG; two 0.30in (7.62mm) MGs

Armor: 0.512in (13mm)

Crew: 3 plus 10

Dimensions: Length 20ft 9in (6.34m); Width 7ft 4in (2.22m); Height 7ft 6in (2.28m)

Weight: 9.33 tons (9477kg)

Powerplant: White 160AX 6–cylinder inline, gasoline, 143hp (106.7kW)

Speed: 45mph (72km/h)

Range: 200 miles (322km)

✖ 1939 Germany

SDKFZ 250 ARMORED PERSONNEL CARRIER

Popular, reliable, and highly versatile, the SdKfz 250 remained in production until the end of World War II. It was expensive to produce, but proved itself to be excellent value for money.

Below: This SdKfz is pictured in France in 1944.

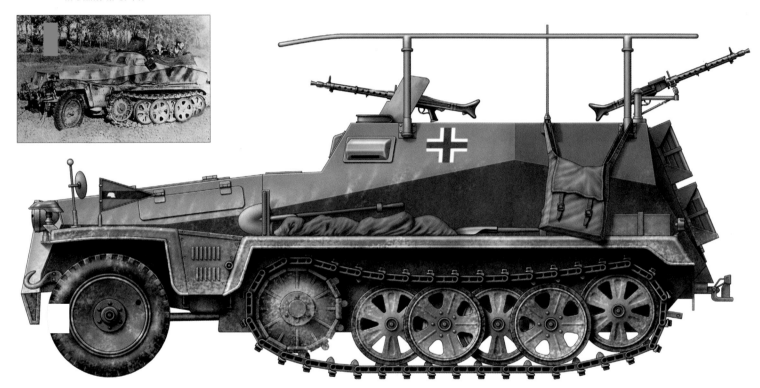

Specifications

(SdKfz 250/1)

Armament: Two 0.312in (7.92mm) MGs

Armor: Maximum, 0.57in (14.5mm)

Crew: 2 plus 4 troops

Dimensions: Length 14ft 11.5in (4.56m); Width 6ft 4.75in (1.95m); Height 5ft 5.4in (1.66m)

Weight: approx 5.61 tons (5700kg)

Powerplant: Maybach HL42 TRKM, 6-cylinder gasoline, 100hp (74.5kW)

Speed: Road, 40.4mph (65km/h)

Range: Road, 217.5 miles (350km)

The SdKfz 250 light armored personnel carrier stemmed from the same design that resulted in the SdKfz 251, which was a heavier vehicle. The design worked toward two types of APC, a one-tonner and a three-tonner, and it was the former that was produced as the SdKfz 250. The chassis was made by Demag AG of Wetter (in the Rühr) and was based on that of the SdKfz 10 truck. The armored body was made by Büssing-NAG. Production of the SdKfz 250/1 started in June 1941. This vehicle carried half a platoon (six men) and two machine guns. It was followed by various other models, which included versions armed with a variety of weapons ranging from a 3.19in (81mm) mortar to a 0.79in (20mm) cannon.

Above: The SdKfz 250 was produced in many versions through the war and could be armed with a wide variety of weapons; this one has two MG34 machine guns.

SdKfz 250/9

A much-improved model appeared in 1942 in the form of the SdKfz 250/9. Three prototypes were sent to Russia for operational trials, where they were found to be much more effective than the SdKfz 222. Production of the latter was therefore discontinued, and mass production of the SdKfz 250/9 began in May 1943. Some SdKfz 250s were converted to the role of tank destroyer, armed with a 1.46in (37mm) antitank gun.

KV-1 HEAVY TANK

The KV-1 was the only type of Soviet tank capable of holding its own against the Panzers when Germany invaded the Soviet Union in June 1941. It was produced only in small numbers.

At the time of its appearance in 1941, the Klim-Voroshilov KV-1 was the most formidable tank in the world. It was developed in 1938 as a successor to the T-35, taking its name from Klimenti Voroshilov, who was then the Commissar for Defense. The tank was evaluated under operational conditions in the war with Finland, and ordered into production as the KV-1A (with a long-barrel 3in [76.2mm] gun) and the KV-2 (with a 4.8in [122mm] main armament, which made the tank very ponderous to use). The KV-2 had a tall, slab-sided turret that made a tempting target for enemy gunners and rendered the tank vulnerable. The KV-1, however, was a formidable vehicle that served the Red Army well during the most dangerous period of the war on the Eastern Front. Its biggest drawback was that it suffered from a lack of mobility, which caused problems on the vast open spaces of the Russian plain. It was at its most useful in forming the spearhead of an armored attack, when it was used as a battering-ram to break through enemy defenses, creating a gap that could then be exploited by T-34s.

Specifications

(KV-I Model 1942)

Armament: One 3in (76.2mm) L/41 ZiS-5 gun; three or four 0.3in (7.62mm) DT MGs (bow, coaxial, turret rear, and occasionally commander's cupola)

Armor: 1.18–2.95in (30–75mm)

Crew: 5

Dimensions: Length 21ft 11in (6.68m); Width 10ft 11in (3.32m); Height 8ft 11in (2.71m)

Weight: 42.3 tons (43,000kg)

Powerplant: V2K V-12 diesel, 550bhp (410kW) at 2150rpm

Speed: 21.7mph (35km/h) (rarely achieved)

Range: 93 miles (150km)

Left: This photograph gives a good impression of the size and bulk of the KV-1, which struck terror into its opponents.

Below: The Soviet KV-1 heavy tank was the most powerful tank in the world when it first appeared, and was mainly used to break through strongly fortified positions. Its principal drawback was that it was slow and ponderous.

T-34 TANK

Arguably, no tank in the history of warfare has come as a greater shock to the enemy, nor inflicted more terror, than did the T-34 when it first appeared on the Russian Front in the summer of 1941.

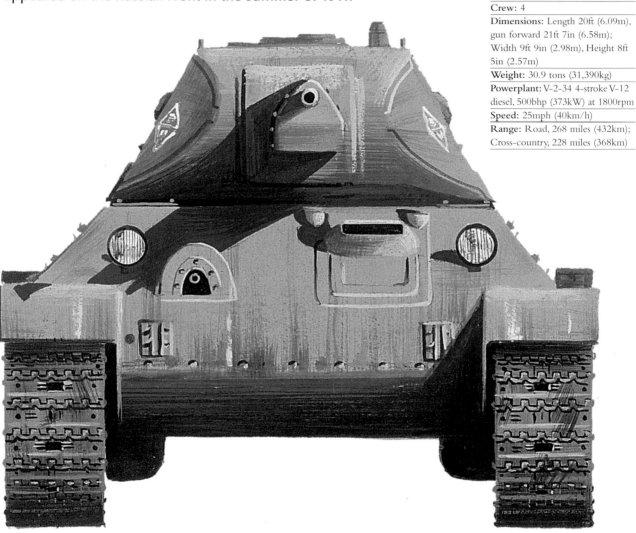

Specifications

(T-34/76 1941)

Armament: 3in (76.2mm) L/41.2 F-34 rifled gun; two 0.3in (7.62mm) Degtaryev DT MGs (one coaxial, one hull-mounted)

Armor: 1.89in (47mm) (hull front), 2.56in (65mm) (turret front)

Crew: 4

Dimensions: Length 20ft (6.09m), gun forward 21ft 7in (6.58m); Width 9ft 9in (2.98m), Height 8ft 5in (2.57m)

Weight: 30.9 tons (31,390kg)

Powerplant: V-2-34 4-stroke V-12 diesel, 500bhp (373kW) at 1800rpm

Speed: 25mph (40km/h)

Range: Road, 268 miles (432km); Cross-country, 228 miles (368km)

The T-34 boasted a very advanced design for its day and was the result of the continual upgrading and refinement of the less-than-successful BT-7. This upgrading produced two designs known as the A-20 and A-30—both developments of the BT-1S. These were rejected in favor of the T-32—a cruiser tank with a more powerful gun and heavier armor. It appeared in 1939 and had most of the features of the T-34. The vehicle

was designed by a group under the leadership of Mikhail Ilyich Koshkin. He was a sick man with less than two years to live, but embarked on updating the armor of the T-32. This became the T-34.

Common sense

The new tank was the product of robust common sense, and owed its existence to a team of men who could envisage a

Above: *The business end of a T-34. Note the sloping armor, an innovation that made most German antitank projectiles ineffective when the T-34 first entered combat in the summer of 1941.*

Above: *The T-34 was not a tank for crew comfort; it was dirty, noisy, smelly, and very functional. The driver's hatch is shown in this photograph, together with the tank's main armament.*

Variants

The T-34 was produced in many variants and was the second most widely produced tank of all time. The most widely produced was its successor, the T-54/55. The T-34/8, appeared in 1943. It was an improved model and it was this version that opened the gates to the flood of Soviet armor which, after the battle of Kursk in July 1943, began to roll westward to the frontiers of Germany. By 1945, the T-34 had replaced nearly every type of Russian tank in production. After World War II, T-34s equipped the armies of many countries within the Soviet sphere of influence, and in 1950 a full brigade of 120 T-34s spearheaded the North Korean attack on South Korea. In all, 39 countries used the T-34, and production only ended in 1958 after many thousands had been issued. Most recently, the T-34 was used in the conflicts in the former Yugoslavia, and some T-34s acquired by Cuba saw action in Angola.

mid-20th-century battlefield much more clearly than any of their Western counterparts. The T-34 went into mass production in late 1940 as the T-34/76A. By the time of the German invasion of the Soviet Union in June 1941, it was already well established. The long and fluid nature of the front meant that it was initially used at the points of greatest danger, leaving older tanks to try to stem the German advance elsewhere.

Below: *A profile of the T34. Later models of the T-34 were instrumental in turning the tide of war on the Eastern Front, and was a match for the formidable German Panther. It remained in use long after the war with Soviet satellite countries and in Africa.*

✂ 1940 UK

MARK III VALENTINE INFANTRY TANK

The Valentine was one of the most successful pre-World War II tank designs. It was used widely, and proved a valuable asset in the desert, where it first saw action in 1941.

Specifications

Armament: One 2pdr (1.57in/40mm) gun; one 0.31in (7.92mm) Besa MG

Armor: 0.32–2.56in (8–65mm)

Crew: 3

Dimensions: Length 19ft 4in (5.89m); Width 8ft 8in (2.63m); Height 7ft 6in (2.273m)

Weight: 17 tons (17,272kg)

Powerplant: AEC 6-cylinder diesel 131bhp (97.73kW), or AEC 6-cylinder gasoline 135bhp (180.9kW), or GMS 6-cylinder diesel 135bhp (180.9kW)

Speed: 14.9mph (24km/h)

Range: 90 miles (145km)

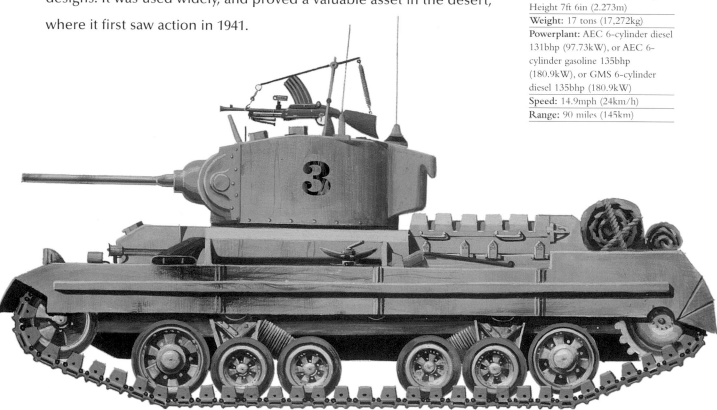

In 1938, Vickers was asked to produce a new infantry tank based on the A10 design, and in July 1939 the new vehicle was ordered into production as the Infantry Tank Mk III Valentine. It carried heavier armor than the A10, and incorporated many improvements as a result of the problems that the earlier tank had experienced.

Mass production

The Valentine was rushed into mass production in 1940 in the aftermath of the loss of British armor during the fighting in France. It was first used in the Western Desert during Operation Crusader (the British offensive to relieve Tobruk) in November 1941, by which time it had become one of the most important armored fighting vehicles in the British Army. By early 1944, when production ceased, 8375 units had been produced. The tank was also produced in Canada, although most of the Canadian output was sent to the Soviet Union. The Valentine proved readily adaptable to various roles and numerous variants were produced, ranging from bridge-layers to self-propelled guns. Many Valentines saw service in the Burma campaign, where they were superior to the Japanese types in service.

Right: An early model Mk V Valentine receives a good deal of attention in Valletta as Malta celebrates the birthday of King George VI in 1943. The Valentine saw service worldwide.

Above: *The Valentine Mk III was mass produced from 1940 and took part in all the campaigns in the Western Desert.*

⚒ 1940 USA

M3A1 STUART LIGHT TANK

The M3A1 light tank was the main combat version of the M2/M3 light tank series in service with the US Army when the United States entered the war in December 1941.

Below: Built to replace the M2 light tank, the M3 was little more than an upgrade of that design. It quickly proved to be undergunned and underarmored, but it was built in large numbers.

Specifications

(M5 model)

Armament: One 1.46in (37mm) M6 gun; three 0.30in (7.62mm) MGs

Armor: 2.5in (64mm)

Crew: 4

Dimensions: Length 14ft 3in (4.34m); Width 7ft 5in (2.25m); Height 7ft 7in (2.3m)

Weight: 14.7 tons (14,969kg)

Powerplant: Two Cadillac Series 42 V-8 110hp (82kW) each

Speed: 37mph (58km/h)

Range: 100 miles (161km)

Right: The M3A1 was used in all theaters of war. It was robust and reliable, performing well in all types of terrain. The British nicknamed it the "Honey."

After the fighting in France in 1940 had been assessed by neutral US observers, it was realized the M2 light tank was becoming rapidly obsolete, and steps were taken to improve it by adding thicker armor and incorporating a new suspension system to cope with the extra weight. The revised vehicle was designated M3A1. It entered production in 1941. The British Army was the first to use it in combat and it fought widely during World War II.

Jeb Stuart

It was the British who named it the Stuart, after the Civil War General Jeb Stuart. About 170 Stuart tanks took part in Operation Crusader, the desert battle of November 1941, and although British tank crews complained about the weakness of its 1.46in (37mm) gun they praised its handling and reliability, which earned it the nickname "Honey." In American service, it first saw combat in the Philippines in 1942. The M3 was gradually replaced by an improved version with two Cadillac engines, the M5, from 1942, and in 1944 it was succeeded by the Light Tank M24. Many M3s were supplied to the Soviet Union, where, despite its deficiencies, it was superior to the equivalent Russian tanks then in service.

⚒ 1941 UK

CHURCHILL MARK IV INFANTRY TANK

The Churchill was without doubt the most important British tank to be produced in World War II, and gave rise to more variants than any other model. Its variations were crucial to the success of D-Day.

The Churchill tank was issued in 1939. It was the result of a request for a heavy AFV capable of breaking through obstacles, as the tanks of World War I were intended to do. During trials, however, it became apparent that a lighter tank would be needed, and so a revised specification was issued and allocated to Vauxhall Motors, who designed the Infantry Tank Mk IV, later to be named the Churchill. Starting from scratch, Vauxhall designed a well-armored tank with large, sturdy tracks. The design was completed by July 1940 and, with Britain in real danger of invasion following the collapse of France, the Churchill was ordered into production before its capability had been

Above: This artwork shows some of the Churchill's interior, including the driver's position, the gun breech, the engine compartment, and the suspension.

fully assessed. Many shortcomings were quickly revealed, including an engine that was underpowered and the same weak two-pounder gun that had been fitted to the earlier cruiser tanks. It put up a disastrous performance when it was first used in combat in support of the abortive and costly Dieppe landing operation in August 1942.

Variants

The tank was soon to vindicate itself with the Mk III version, however. Armed with a

Specifications

Armament: One 2pdr (1.57in/40mm) gun; two 0.31in (7.92mm) Besa MGs
Armor: 0.63–4.02in (16–102mm)
Crew: 5
Dimensions: Length 24ft 5in (7.442m); Width 11ft 4in (3.45m); Height 9ft (2.74m)
Weight: 39 tons (39,660kg)
Powerplant: Bedford Twin Six, 350bhp (261.1kW)
Speed: 14.9mph (24km/h)
Range: 88 miles (140km)

Right: *The Churchill was the most important British tank to go into production during World War II, and many different variants were produced. The specialized versions were to prove invaluable on D-Day.*

Below: *This photograph illustrates the Churchill's angular lines. It was a classic infantry tank, slow but heavily armored, and was more difficult to knock out than the American Sherman.*

six-pounder gun, this was deployed to the Western Desert in time to take part in the decisive Battle of El Alamein in October 1942. The success of the Churchill continued, and a 2.95in (75mm) gun was introduced in the Mk VI version. The addition of more armor produced the Mk VII, which first went into action in support

of the Normandy landings in June 1944, and it was at this time that the special versions of the Churchill came into their own. These included the Churchill Mk III AVRE (Armoured Vehicle Royal Engineers, designed to knock out pillboxes and blockhouses at short range with its "flying dustbin" mortar bombs), the Churchill Mk III "Bobbin" (which could lay down a canvas mat 109 yards [100m] long to provide a road for vehicles over a soft beach surface), the Churchill Mk III bridge layer, and, most horrific and spectacular of all, the Churchill Mk VIII "Crocodile" (a flamethrowing tank that carried 400 gallons [1818 litres] of flame-gun fuel in a towed trailer). Compressed nitrogen forced the fuel from trailer to flame-gun, which was mounted in the normal machine-gun position, giving a range of about 120 yards (131m). The Churchill remained in first-line service with the British Army until 1952, and second-line recovery vehicles were not retired until 1965.

M3 GRANT/LEE MEDIUM TANK

The M3 medium tank was a hurried design, but it was armed with a powerful 2.95in (75mm) gun. It finally gave the Allies a fighting chance in combat against the Panzers.

Above: *This photograph clearly shows the position of the M3's 2.95in (75mm) gun in its sponson mounted on the right of the hull. This example has a modified turret.*

Specifications

(M3 medium tank [Lee Mk I])
Armament: One 2.95in (75mm) M2 or M3 cannon; one 1.46in (37mm) M5 or M6 cannon; four 0.30in (7.62mm) MGs

Armor: 2.24in (57mm)

Crew: 6

Dimensions: Length 18ft 6in (5.64m); Width 8ft 11in (2.72m); Height 10ft 3in (3.12m)

Weight: 26.7 tons (27,216kg)

Powerplant: Continental R-975-EC2 or E1 radial gasoline, 340hp (253.5kW)

Speed: 26mph (42km/h)

Range: 120 miles (193km)

The action of the German Panzers in France rendered the existing American tanks obsolete.

As a result of this, the American Army issued a specification for a new tank armed with a 2.95in (75mm) gun. This eventually materialized as the M4 Sherman, but in the interim they took the existing M2 and modified it, retaining the 1.46in (37mm) turret but adding a new 2.95in (75mm) main armament mounted in a sponson on the right-hand side of the hull. The redesigned tank was ordered into mass production. The British Army ordered it in large numbers to replace lost armor.

Above: *Designed to fill the gap until deployment of the M4 Sherman, the M3 Grant gave a massive boost to British Commonwealth forces in the Western Desert.*

General Grant

In British service the vehicle, which was fitted with a modified turret with a lower profile, was named the General Grant, while unaltered vehicles were named General Lee. The M3 went into action for the first time in the Western Desert in 1942, bringing much improved firepower to the Commonwealth armored divisions. Production of the M3 ended in December 1942, by which time 6258 units had been produced.

1942 Australia

SENTINEL AUSTRALIAN CRUISER MARK I

Although it was produced hastily as a "panic measure," the Australian AC1 Sentinel, based on the American M3, was an effective AFV and would have acquitted itself well in combat.

The Sentinel Australian Cruiser Mk I was designed mainly in response to the outbreak of war in Europe. The war not only deprived Australia of defense materials normally shipped from England, but also made northern Australia vulnerable to the threat of a Japanese invasion. Attacks on Darwin and other targets in 1942 made this threat very real.

Specifications

Designs were drawn up following orders for a cruiser tank armed with a two-pounder (1.57in/40mm) gun and using as many components as possible of the American M3. The tank, first known as Australian Cruiser I (ACI), had an all-cast hull and was powered by three Cadillac engines. The first models were ready by January 1942, and received the name Sentinel. A follow-on version (the Sentinel AC3) was armed with a 25-pounder (3.45in/87.6mm) gun in place of the inadequate two-pounder (1.57in/40mm). However, this would clearly be ineffective against armor and so production switched to the Sentinel AC4, armed with a 17-pounder (3in/76.2mm) antitank gun in 1943. The Sentinel was never used in combat, but some vehicles, masquerading as Panzers, featured in the film *The Rats Of Tobruk*.

Left: The Sentinel's original two-pounder gun was too puny to be effective, so successive models were armed with the 25-pounder and, ultimately, the 17-pounder antitank weapon.

Specifications

Armament: One 2pdr (1.57in/40mm) gun; two 0.3in (7.62mm) MGs

Armor: 2.6in (65mm)

Crew: 5

Dimensions: Length 20ft 9in (6.4m); Width 9ft 1in (2.8m); Height: 8ft 5in (2.59m)

Weight: 28 tons (28,489kg)

Powerplant: Three Cadillac V-8 gasoline engines, 117bhp (87kW), in cloverleaf layout

Speed: 30mph (48km/h)

Range: 198 miles (319km)

Left: Despite the fact that it was rushed into production, the Sentinel was a remarkably effective design with many innovations. This is the AC4, which had a 17-pounder gun.

1942 Germany

PANZERKAMPFWAGEN V PANTHER

The Panther was intended as a counter to the T-34. Although it was probably the best German tank to emerge during World War II, it was too complex to build quickly enough.

By the end of 1941 it had become clear to the German General Staff that something had to be done to redress the armored balance with Russia. This was tilting in the Russians' favor thanks to the deployment of the T-34, which was more than a match for the Panzer IV. Two German companies—Daimler-Benz and MAN of Augsburg—were given the task of designing a powerful new tank, and the MAN design was accepted in May 1942. By September 1942 a prototype was being tested, and the vehicle, designated Panzerkampfwagen V Panther (SdKfz 171) was ordered into immediate production.

Specifications

(PzKpfw V Ausführung G)

Armament: One 2.95in (75mm) gun; three 0.312in (7.92mm) MGs

Armor: Maximum, hull, 3.15in (80mm)

Crew: 5

Dimensions: Length 29ft 1in (8.865m); Width 11ft 3in (3.43m); Height 9ft 9in (2.97m)

Weight: 44.75 tons (45,465kg)

Powerplant: Maybach HL230P30, V-12 gasoline, 700hp (522kW)

Speed: Road, 34mph (54.7km/h)

Range: Road, 110 miles (177km)

Below: *Cutaway showing the interior of the Panther V. Without doubt the best German tank of World War II, the Panther was hampered by its complexity, which created many problems on operations. The complicated nature of the vehicle is apparent in this illustration.*

Above: *The Panther was rushed into production without proper trials, and numerous faults soon became apparent. In its early days, more Panthers were lost through technical failure than enemy action.*

Combat

The Panther was first used in the Battle of Kursk in July 1943 and did not perform well. It was plagued with a number of problems. On July 10, only 38 Panthers were serviceable out of 200 deployed with XLVIII Panzer Korps. Once these early problems were solved, however, the Panther became a formidable fighting machine. It was widely used in Normandy in the weeks after D-Day as well as on the Russian Front. Some vehicles were used by the French Army for some time after World War II.

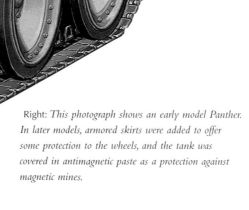

Right: *This photograph shows an early model Panther. In later models, armored skirts were added to offer some protection to the wheels, and the tank was covered in antimagnetic paste as a protection against magnetic mines.*

⚒ **1942 Germany**

PANZERKAMPFWAGEN VI TIGER I

The Tiger I tank was developed in some haste in 1941. It was designed to combat the Russian KV-1, and was first used in the fall of 1942. It was so impressive that it tended to dominate the enemy whenever it appeared.

Although it was a brilliant, robust design, featured a 700hp (514.3kW) engine, and had a gearbox with eight forward and four reverse gears, the Tiger I showed serious deficiencies under operational conditions. It had a range of only 70 miles (112.7km) and despite the ingenious interleaving of bogies in the torsion bar suspension to enhance mobility, it was incompatible with the fast-moving Panzer divisions. This meant that it was rejected by the German tank leaders, who preferred the more mobile, smaller tanks which could be manufactured in greater quantity. Despite this, the Tiger I could easily afford to exchange shots with most enemy tanks at long range, and it had a deep-wading capability, which was unique among German tanks.

Above: It is easy to see why the Tiger spread terror among its opponents wherever it appeared. The whole configuration of the tank exudes menace, and its enemies must have despaired of finding the means to counter it.

Right: *The Tiger I represented a new approach that emphasized firepower and armor at the expense of mobility, but this was not critical as it could knock out most Allied tanks while remaining outside the range of their guns.*

Specifications

Armament: One 3.46in (88mm) gun; two or three 0.312in (7.92mm) MGs

Armor: Maximum, hull, 3.94in (100mm)

Crew: 5

Dimensions: Length 27ft 8.675in (8.45m); Width 11ft 3.8in (3.56m); Height 9ft 10in (3m)

Weight: Combat, approx 56 tons (56,900kg)

Powerplant: Maybach HL230P45, V-12 gasoline, 700hp (514.3kW)

Speed: Road, 23mph (37km/h)

Range: Road, 121 miles (195km)

Below: *A Tiger I advancing along a typical dirt road in Russia. When the dirt turned to mud, and the mud froze like concrete to the tracks, the Tiger was always in danger of becoming immobilized.*

Geographical use

The Tiger I was originally named as the PzKw VI Ausführung H, although it was commonly known simply as the Tiger. The Tiger I—despite a number of technical problems that combined to reduce its operational efficiency—performed very well on the Eastern Front and in Tunisia. Comparatively few, however, were used in North Africa, as a result of air and submarine attacks from Malta on the Axis supply convoys.

Design

The Tiger I had frontal armor up to 4.72in (120mm) thick, with 3.15in (80mm) on the sides and back, and this proved very effective at stopping rounds from most antitank guns. The Tiger could knock out its most common opponents (the T-34, Sherman, and Churchill IV) at ranges exceeding 1600 yards, whereas the T-34 could not penetrate the frontal armor at any range, although it could penetrate the Tiger's side armor at a range of 500 yards or less. This was also true of the M4 Sherman. Wherever possible, this tank engaged a Tiger in units of four or more to get in close enough for a kill. In the later stages of World War II, the biggest threat to the Tiger was the rocket-armed fighter bomber. Even then, this was not sufficiently accurate to be sure of a kill against a single vehicle, but was reasonably effective against concentrations of tanks.

Withdrawal

The Tiger I was phased out from January 1944, with the introduction of the Panzerkampfwagen VI Tiger II Ausführung B. By this time, 1355 models had been built.

⚒ **1942 Soviet Union**

SU-76 ASSAULT GUN

The SU-76 was a hurried wartime conversion of the T-70 light tank, fitted with a 3in (76.2mm) gun. It was produced in large numbers and proved its success on the Eastern Front in 1943.

The SU-76 was something of an expedient. It was ordered into production at a time when the Soviet Army, having suffered massive losses in the second half of 1941, was in desperate need of AFVs. It was produced to help the Russian forces stem the German advance. One weapon to do this was the Zis-3 3in (76mm) artillery piece, which also had an excellent antitank capability. As the fighting so far had shown that Russian light tanks were virtually useless in combat, the T-70 light tank (already on the production line) was converted as a vehicle for the Zis-3 gun. The end product was the SU-76. "SU" denoted Samokhodnaya Ustanovka, or self-propelled mounting.

Above: *A conversion of the T-70 light tank, the SU-76 was rushed into production as a desperate attempt to find some means of engaging the latest German Panzers.*

Use of SU-76

Some necessary modification to the T-70 chassis meant that the SU-76 did not enter production until late 1942, and it was mid-1943 before it was issued to the Red Army. An early batch had been rebuilt with a different engine drive system. It subsequently performed very well, although it was completely lacking in comfort and disliked by its crews. The SU-76 was supplied to several Soviet satellite countries after the war.

Specifications

Armament: One 3in (76.2mm) Zis-3 L/41 gun

Armor: 0.39–1.37in (10–35mm)

Crew: 4

Dimensions: Length 16ft 5in (5m); Width 8ft 10in (2.7m); Height 6ft 11in (2.1m)

Weight: 10 tons (10,200kg)

Powerplant: Two GAZ-203 6-cylinder gasoline engines, 138bhp (103kW) at 3400rpm

Speed: 28mph (45km/h)

Range: 199 miles (320km)

1942 USA

M10 TANK DESTROYER

The American M10 was produced in greater numbers than any other US AFV of its kind. It was the main armament of the US Army's tank destroyer battalions, and was also used by the British, French, and Italians.

Right: *The M10 was intended to be the principal weapon in the armory of the US Army's Tank Destroyer Command. Although relatively lightly armored, the M10 was fast and agile. In British Army service the M10 was called the Wolverine.*

Specifications

Armament: One 3in (76mm) M7 gun; one 0.50in (12.7mm) MG
Armor: 1.46in (37mm)
Crew: 5
Dimensions: Length (with gun) 19ft 7in (5.97m); Width 10ft (3.05m); Height 8ft 2in (2.49m)
Weight: 28.6 tons (29,028kg)
Powerplant: Two GMS6-71 diesels
Speed: 30mph (48km/h)
Range: 200 miles (322km)

The M10 was the result of a very sound tactical concept developed in the 1930s by the US Army. This planned for a tank destroyer force comprising both towed and self-propelled antitank guns. It was intended to be deployed *en masse* to disrupt an armored attack, leaving tanks to perform an infantry support role. One of the first vehicles to meet this requirement was the 3in (76mm) Gun Motor Carriage M10, which used the main chassis of the M4A2 Sherman medium tank, surmounted by an M7 3in (76mm) gun in a turret with a 360-degree traverse.

Production

The M10 went into production in September 1942. America's production capacity was large enough that 4993 units came off the assembly line before the end of the year, when production ceased. Most of these vehicles were issued to the US Army's 106 tank destroyer battalions. The tank was also used by the British Army (who named it the Wolverine) and later by the Free French and Italian Co-Belligerent forces. The British fitted the excellent 17-pounder antitank guns to some of their M10s, which were then named Achilles.

Below: *Late in the war the M10 was supplemented by a developed version, the M36, seen here. The M36 mounted a 3.54in (90mm) gun, still mounted in an open-topped turret.*

⚒ 1942 USA

M4 SHERMAN COMBAT TANK

The M4 Sherman was the first truly effective combat tank produced by

the United States, and was greatly superior to its predecessor, the M3.

It proved to be a match for the Panzer IVF.

Armed with an excellent dual-purpose 2.95in (76mm) gun, the Sherman M4A1 finally gave the Allies a tank that could outmatch the German 3.46in (88mm) antitank gun, which had proved deadly when engaging earlier AFVs. Several different versions were produced: Some Shermans had very reliable diesel engines, while others had gasoline radial engines, originally made for aircraft. The gasoline-engined variants were unpopular. They were prone to catching fire after being hit. The Germans nicknamed them "Tommy Cookers," after a portable stove used in the previous war, or "Ronsons," after the famous brand of lighter. Another problem was that the Sherman could be very difficult to evacuate, especially if the main gun turret came to rest at the wrong angle and prevented one or the other of the forward hatches from being opened.

Above: *A wartime photograph of a US Sherman tank crew during a training exercise before the D-Day landings.*

Specifications

Armament: One 2.95in (75mm) gun; one 0.5in (12.7mm) MG; two 0.30in (7.62mm) MGs

Armor: 2.44in (62mm)

Crew: 5

Dimensions: Length 19ft 4in (5.88m); Width 8ft 7in (2.68m); Height 9m (2.74m)

Weight: 74.5 tons (75,705kg)

Powerplant: Wright R-975-C1, radial, 9-cylinder

Speed: 24mph (39km/h)

Range: 100 miles (160km)

Right: *Shermans disembarking from a Landing Ship (Tank). The name Sherman was bestowed on the M4 by the British, who used large numbers, from the desert to the final battles in northwest Europe.*

Below: *The Sherman Crab was the most widely-used mine clearance flail tank of World War II. Other tanks were also fitted with flails, but the Sherman was the preferred carrier.*

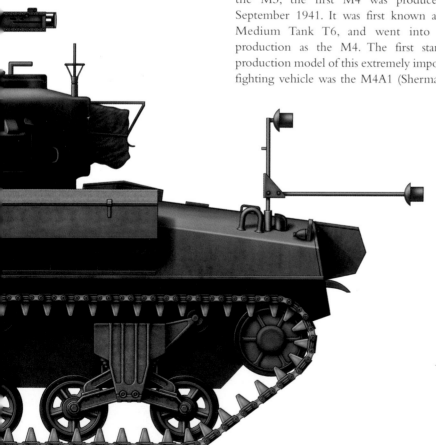

Production

Using the same basic hull and suspension as the M3, the first M4 was produced in September 1941. It was first known as the Medium Tank T6, and went into mass production as the M4. The first standard production model of this extremely important fighting vehicle was the M4A1 (Sherman II) with a fully cast rather than a cast/welded hull; other main variants were the M4A2 (Sherman III) with a welded hull, the M4A3 (Sherman IV) and the M4A4 (Sherman V). Some of the later versions mounted a 2.99in (76mm) gun. All versions had different engines, all progressively more powerful. The British Army acquired large numbers of Shermans, and took them into action for the first time at the Battle of El Alamein in October 1942. As they had done with the Churchill tank, the British modified numbers of Shermans for special tasks, such as flamethrowing and clearing paths through minefields.

Shortcomings

Although the Sherman had the edge over the Panzer IV, it stood little chance in a one-to-one encounter with later German AFVs like the Tiger and Panther, which had strengthened armor and formidable firepower. The Sherman-equipped units suffered heavy losses when they came up against Tigers for the first time in Tunisia. This scenario was repeated in Normandy a year later, following the D-Day landings. What the Sherman lacked in armor and firepower, however, was made up by sheer weight of numbers; over 40,000 had been produced when production ceased in 1945.

⚒ **1943 Germany**

JAGDPANZER IV TANK DESTROYER

The Jagdpanzer IV was a tank-hunting version of the PzKpfw IV. It was armed with a 2.95in (75mm) gun housed in a low-profile superstructure formed from well-sloped armored plates.

Specifications

Armament: One 2.95in (75mm) antitank gun; one or two 0.312in (7.92mm) MGs

Armor: Maximum, 2.36in (60mm)

Crew: 4

Dimensions: Length 22ft 5.7in (6.85m); Width 10ft 4.8in (3.17m); Height 6ft 0.8in (1.85m)

Weight: approx 23.62 tons (24,000kg)

Powerplant: Maybach HL120TRM, V-12 gasoline, 265hp (197.6kW)

Speed: Road, 24.8mph (40km/h)

Range: Road, 130.5 miles (210km)

Germany's military planners became convinced that the guns of existing close support artillery AFVs needed to be radically improved if they were to be effective. This decision was taken in the light of combat experience gained during the campaigns of 1942, particularly in the Soviet Union, where German armor was coming up against increasing numbers of T-34 tanks. The gun that was selected was the 2.95in (75mm) long-barrel weapon, and was the same that had been produced to arm the Panther tank. To install this gun in carriers such as the Panzer III would, however, require much modification and consequent delay, so the Panzer IV's larger chassis was used as the basis of the new Jagdpanzer IV. This became operational in October 1943 and immediately found favor with its crews, not least because of its effective armor protection and the low silhouette of its hull, making it a difficult target.

Early and later versions

Early production Jagdpanzer IVs were still fitted with the muzzle brake. Later versions used a much longer 2.95in (75mm) gun (although this had the effect of overloading the chassis) and also used side armor plating.

Below: *The Jagdpanzer IV was a tank-killer variant of the well-proven Panzer Mk IV and housed its 2.95in (75mm) gun in a superstructure formed from well-sloped armoured plates.*

✖ **1943 Germany**

TIGER II (PANZERKAMPFWAGEN VI)

The Tiger II, sometimes called the King Tiger or Royal Tiger, was the most formidable tank used in World War II. Its main problem was that it was slow and cumbersome, and lacked mobility.

Specifications

Armament: One 3.46in (88mm) gun; two 0.312in (7.92mm) MGs

Armor: Maximum, hull, 5.9in (150mm)

Crew: 5

Dimensions: Length 33ft 8.9in (10.286m); Width 11ft 10.7in (3.625m); Height 10ft 0.9in (3.075m)

Weight: approx 66.93 tons (68,000kg)

Powerplant: Maybach HL230P30, V-12 gasoline, 700hp (514.3kW)

Speed: Road, 21.75mph (35km/h)

Range: Road, 105 miles (170km)

The Tiger II (PzKpfw VI) combined the heavy armor of the Tiger I with the sloped armor of the Panther and was, in effect, a completely different vehicle from the Tiger I. It first went into action in Normandy in July 1944, and was used on the Eastern Front the following month. The Tiger II, sometimes called the King Tiger, was the most powerful tank to be deployed anywhere during World War II, and together with the Panther it formed the spearhead of the German offensive in the Ardennes in December 1944. This drove a dangerous wedge between the Allied armies. Fortunately, the offensive petered out for lack of fuel and many Tigers were abandoned by their crews.

Above: The Tiger II was a formidable fighting machine, but its weak points were that it could be rendered immobile by freezing mud clogging its suspension.

Problems

Despite its success in combat, the Tiger continued to experience many problems, not least of which were caused by its overlapping wheel suspension, which became easily clogged with mud. This had the potential for dire consequences, especially in the Russian winter, when the mud froze and had to be chipped away before the tank was ready for action. The Tiger II chassis was used as the basis for the Jagdtiger B, 48 of which were built. This was armed with a 5.04in (128mm) gun.

Above: A King Tiger battalion preparing to move off. These Tigers are fitted with Porsche turrets; some had turrets developed by Henschel. The long-barreled 3.46in (88mm) gun could fire both armor-piercing and HE ammunition.

⚒ **1943   Soviet Union**

IS-1 HEAVY TANK

The Iosif Stalin (IS) tank was named after the leader of the Soviet Union.
It was developed from the KV-85, which was a version of the KV-1. The IS
tanks were the most powerful to serve in the Red Army in World War II.

Above: *The IS-3 tank, which
supplanted the IS-2 in service
during 1944, was the heaviest
Soviet wartime tank of all, and
spearheaded the breakthrough
into Berlin in April 1945.*

Specifications

(IS-1, 1943)

Armament: One 3.35in (85mm)
gun; two 0.3in (7.62mm) DT MGs

Armor: 1.18–5.2in (30–132mm)

Crew: 4

Dimensions: Length 27ft 3in
(8.32m); Width 10ft 8in (3.25m);
Height 9ft 6in (2.9m)

Weight: 45.3 tons (46,000kg)

Powerplant: V-2-IS 12-cylinder
diesel, 510bhp (380kW)

Speed: 24.8mph (40km/h)

Range: 155 miles (250km)

The IS-1 was developed from the KV
series of heavy tanks to combat German
AFVs such as the Tiger and Panther. Its
design was named KV-13. Marshal Kliment
Voroshilov had fallen out of political favor,
however, and so the new design was named
Iosif (Joseph) Stalin instead. The first batch,
used for evaluation, was called IS-85. The IS-
1 retained the 3.34in (85mm) gun of the
KV-85, but production models were fitted
with the long 4.8in (122mm) gun. This had
greater penetrating power and also enough
strength to blow off a tank's turret even if it

failed to penetrate the armor. With this
modification the tank became the IS-2, the
first examples of which appeared in 1944. A
further variant, the IS-3, retained the 4.8in
(122mm) gun but had a redesigned, more
rounded turret that resembled an upturned
soup bowl.

Assault on Berlin

The IS tanks were the spearhead of the final
assault on Berlin in April 1945, their power
and protection enabling them to break
through the enemy defense barriers.

Above: Now relegated to museums, the T-34 was the most advanced tank of its kind when it was first deployed in 1941.

T-34/85 TANK

When the T-34/85 went into production in the winter of 1943 and 1944, it was the most formidable tank in service anywhere. It was to be the spearhead of the Red Army's drive to Berlin.

Specifications

Armament: One 3.35in (85mm)
ZiS-S-53 gun; two 0.3in (7.62mm)
DT MGs

Armor: 3.54in (90mm)

Crew: 5

Dimensions: Length 26ft 7in
(8.15m); Width 9ft 7in (2.99m);
Height 9ft (2.74m)

Weight: 31.5 tons (32,000kg)

Powerplant: V-2-34 12-cylinder
diesel, 500bhp (373kW) at 1800 rpm

Speed: 34mph (55km/h)

Range: 190 miles (300km)

During 1942, Soviet factories produced more than 5000 units of the T-34/76 tank, but it became clear that extensive changes had to be made to the existing design if the T-34 was to keep up with the new generation of German AFVs. The existing T-34 chassis was adapted to take a cast, three-man turret, fitted with a much more powerful gun. This was the long 3.35in (85mm) which, like the German 3.46in (88mm), was adapted from an antiaircraft gun. Its performance was roughly similar to that of the 3.46in (88mm) fitted in the Tiger I; the 3.35in (85mm) fired a 21.5lb (9.75) shot at a muzzle velocity of 2600 ft (792m)/sec, compared with the 3.46in (88mm) gun's 22.25lb (10.09kg) shot at 2657 ft (810m)/sec. For the T-34/85 of course, a

Above: Cutaway showing the interior of the T-34/85. A very advanced design for its time, the tank was produced in thousands and proved robust, agile, and very effective in combat.

heavier gun, coupled with increased armor, added up to a heavier tank, which meant a certain loss of operational flexibility. Nevertheless, the vital statistics of the T-34/85 were a tribute to the efficiency of the amended design. Its overall weight rose from 27 tons (27,430kg) to 32 tons (32,510kg), and its effective range dropped from 280 miles (450 km) to about 190 miles (306km). Its speed was a little below 30mph (48.28 km/h), about the same as the Panther. When it entered production in the winter of 1943, it was the most formidable tank in the world.

⚒ **1944 USA**

M26 PERSHING HEAVY TANK

The M26 Pershing Heavy Tank entered operational service in 1945, just too late to have any impact on World War II, but in time to take part in the latter stages of the Pacific War.

Above: *This excellent tank entered service too late to make an impact on the war in Europe, but it saw some action in the Pacific.*

Named after General John "Black Jack" Pershing, who commanded the American Expeditionary Force in France during World War I, the M26 heavy tank was developed primarily to counter the German Panther. This was in widespread operational service in France and outmatched the M4 Pershing—the tank that formed the bulk of the Allied armored forces at the time of the campaign in Normandy. Prior to this, the development of heavy tanks had been accorded low priority in the United States, the main effort being concentrated on medium tanks, in particular the M3/M4 series. When the formidable power of the latest Panzers was assessed in the weeks after D-Day, heavy tank development was given higher priority. Following trials with various

Right: *A group of D Company First Marine Division soldiers, standing on a M-26 tank to spearhead a patrol in search of guerrillas.*

Specifications

Armament: One 3.54in (90mm) M3 gun; one 0.50in (12.7mm); two 0.30in (7.62mm) MGs

Armor: 4in (102mm)

Crew: 5

Dimensions: Length 28ft 3in (8.66m); Width 11ft 6in (3.51m); Height 9ft 1in (2.78m)

Weight: 41.2 tons (41,891kg)

Powerplant: Ford GAF, 500hp (373kW)

Speed: 30mph (48km/h)

Range: 100 miles (161km)

Below: *The Pershing influenced US tank development up to the M60 series.*

saw little action before the end of World War II. Ten tanks assigned to the 3rd Armored Division, however, in one encounter, destroyed two Tigers and a Mark IV from a range of about 1000 yards (914m). One or two examples of so-called "Super Pershings," fitted with a 3.54in (90mm) T15E1 high-velocity gun, also arrived in Europe at a very late stage of the war. One of these took part in an action near Dessau on April 4, 1945, destroying a King Tiger and a Panther. Some also deployed to the Pacific, where they were used in the invasion of Okinawa. Five years later, Pershings saw action in Korea, where they were the only American tank capable of matching the T-34/85s being used by the North Koreans and Chinese. According to official US history, some M26s were removed from museums, being hastily refurbished and returned to service for use in Korea. The bulk of vehicles that were still operational were deployed in Europe.

NATO armored forces

The Pershing formed a valuable addition to NATO's armored forces in the dangerous early years of the Cold War, which could easily have developed into a shooting war over issues such as the Berlin blockade. The tank was the first in a series that led to the M60 of today.

prototypes the first of a new generation of US heavy tanks emerged. This was the Heavy Tank T26E3, selected for production as the Heavy Tank M26.

Geographical use

The first M26 vehicles reached northwest Europe early in 1945. They were assigned to the 3rd and 9th Armored Divisions, but they

⚒ **1944 USA**

M24 LIGHT TANK (CHAFFEE)

The M24 Chaffee was introduced too late to make a significant contribution to World War II, but it fought in later conflicts, including the Korean War and the Indo-Pakistan conflict.

Specifications

Armament: One 2.95in (75mm) M6 gun; one 0.50in (12.7mm) MG; two 0.30in (7.62mm) MGs

Armor: 1.5in (38mm)

Crew: 4 or 5

Dimensions: Length 18ft (5.49m); Width 9ft 8in (2.95m); Height 8ft 1in (2.46m)

Weight: 18 tons (18,371kg)

Powerplant: Two Cadillac 44T24 V-8, 110hp (82kW)

Speed: 34mph (55km/h)

Range: 175 miles (281km)

Below: *The M24 Chaffee light tank, armed with a 2.95in (75mm) gun, was introduced into service in late 1944, and formed the basis of a new family of armored fighting vehicles in the postwar years.*

The M24 light tank (later known as the Chaffee) was a joint venture between the US Ordnance Committee and Cadillac. In March 1943, Cadillac set about developing a new AFV which would eradicate the shortcomings that had become apparent in the M3/M5 series. One of these was the weak 1.46in (37mm) armament, so the new design featured a light tank based on the M5A1, but armed with a 2.95in (75mm) gun. This new vehicle was called the T24, this being changed to M24 when it was accepted for service. Its gun was a derivative of the 2.95in (75mm) weapon developed for the B-25H, the anti-ship version of the North American Mitchell bomber. Production of the Light Tank M24 began in 1944, and 4731 vehicles were eventually produced, some of which were allocated to the British Army.

Above: *The M24 was a good-looking design and was well-armed for its size and weight. This small tank carried a surprisingly large crew of five men—commander, gunner, loader, driver, and radio operator.*

Geographical use

The first M24s were deployed to Europe in December 1944, but did not play an important part in the last months of World War II. They were only available in relatively small numbers and were vulnerable to German tank and antitank guns. They were used in a reconnaissance role during the Korean War, however, with the French in Indo-China and with the Pakistani Army in the 1971 conflict with India.

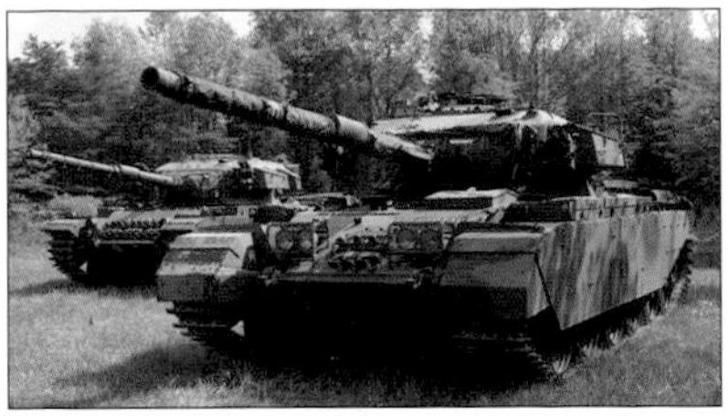

Above: *The Centurion was arguably the best tank to see service in the Korean War. Its biggest asset was the renowned L7 4.124in (105mm) gun, on which many of today's tank guns are based.*

1945 UK

CENTURION (A41) MAIN BATTLE TANK

Originally designed to withstand a direct hit from a 3.46in (88mm) antitank round, the Centurion went on to become one of the most successful battle tanks of the Cold War era.

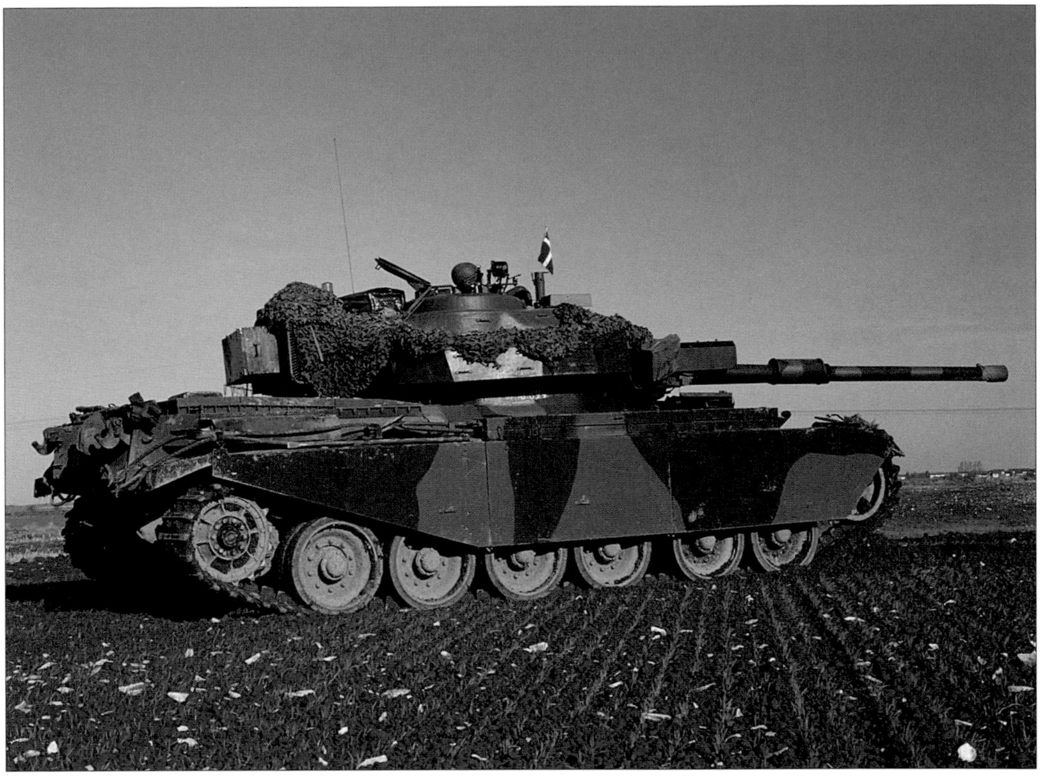

Right: *The Centurion main battle tank incorporated all the lessons learned in the design of earlier generations of British tanks. It was hugely successful, thousands being built for service with armies all over the world.*

Specifications

Armament: One 17pdr (3in/76mm); one coaxial 0.31in (7.92mm) Besa MG or one 0.79in (20mm) Polsten cannon
Armor: 0.75–4in (17–127mm)
Crew: 4
Dimensions: Length 24ft 6in (7.82m); Width 11ft 2in (3.39m); Height 9ft 11in (3.01m)
Weight: 42.5 tons (43,182kg)
Powerplant: Meteor V-12 gasoline, 650bhp (484.7kW)
Speed: 22mph (35km/h)
Range: 120 miles (192km)

Development of the Centurion main battle tank started in 1943, in response to a War Office requirement for a new heavy cruiser tank. One of the principal requirements was that the new AFV should be able to withstand a direct hit from an 3.46in (88mm) gun, but at an early stage of the development program the 40 ton (40,640kg) weight limit (imposed by the capacity of existing transport trailers) had to be increased to fulfill this requirement. The War Office decided to build new trailers rather than hamper the design of what promised to be an excellent tank, so work proceeded on a heavier version. By this time, construction of the first 40-ton prototypes was well advanced, and these were completed as the Centurion Mk I. Only a few of these were produced before production switched to the more heavily armored Centurion Mk II. This was followed by the Mk III, which featured a fully automated stabilization system for its 20-pounder gun. The latter was used only for a short time before it was replaced by an effective 4.13in (105mm) weapon.

Success

The Centurion became one of the world's most successful tanks. It was supplied to many armed forces, and was used in Korea, the Middle East, and Vietnam. When production ended in 1962, 4423 units had been built.

⚒ **1948 Soviet Union**

T-54/55 MAIN BATTLE TANK

The T-54/55 series of main battle tanks has seen more combat than any other post-World War II tank. It was also produced in the largest numbers, many thousands being built.

No other tank in the world has been produced in such quantity as the T-54/55 series. It was developed as the Soviet Union's main battle tank in 1947 and was still serving with some developing-world (and former Soviet-friendly) countries 60 years later. The T-54 was based on the T-44, but with a 3.94in (100mm) gun instead of an 3.34in (85mm) weapon. In service, the tank was progressively updated, the T-54A model being fitted with gun-stabilization and night-vision equipment. The T-55B was the first model to incorporate infrared night-vision equipment and two-axis stabilization for the main gun.

Left: The T-54/55's main armament was originally the D10T 3.9in (100mm) rifled gun, a very large caliber weapon for its time, but long since made obsolete by its inability to penetrate modern armor with the types of armor-piercing ammunition it used.

Specifications

Armament: One 3.94in (100mm)
D-10T gun; two 0.3in (7.62mm)
DT MGs; one 0.5in (12.7mm)
DShK AA MG

Armor: Maximum, 8in (203mm)

Crew: 4

Dimensions: Length (hull) 21ft 2in
(6.45m); Width 10ft 9in (3.27m);
Height 7ft 10in (2.4m)

Weight: 35.42 tons (36,000kg)

Powerplant: V-54 12-cylinder
diesel, 520bhp (388kW) at 2000rpm

Speed: 30mph (48km/h)

Range: 250 miles (400km)

Below: Egyptian Marines operate a Soviet-made T-54 main battle tank during the multinational joint service Exercise Bright Star in 1985.

Design and use

The T-55 was a T-54 modified for operations on the nuclear battlefield. It had a thicker turret casting, more powerful engine, and primitive NBC protection. Production of the T-54/55 continued in the former Soviet Union into the 1980s, and was also undertaken in China (where it was produced as the Type 69), Czechoslovakia, Romania, and Poland. The T-54/55 has been used very widely, particularly in the Middle East during the 1967 Six-Day War and the Yom Kippur War of 1973. During these two conflicts, Israel captured over 1000 T-54/55s and retained many of them for the Israeli Army. They replaced the Soviet 3.94in (100mm) gun with a 4.13in (105mm) L5 or M68 and the Russian engine with a General Motors diesel. In Israeli service the T-54/55 was known as the Tiran-5. After their retirement from reserve units in the 1990s many were sold on to Latin-American countries, while others were modified as armored personnel carriers.

Above: East German T-54 training tanks in operation. Like many Warsaw Pact forces, the East German army continued to rely on the T-54/55 rather than convert entirely to the T-62.

Export

The T-54/55 was exported to over 40 countries, while China exported thousands of her Type 69 variant. Many of these were delivered to Iran and Iraq, and fought during the long "oil war" between those two countries in the 1980s. Most of the Iraqi tanks were destroyed during the Gulf War of 1991, where their encounters with American M1 Abrams and British Challenger main battle tanks were short, brutal, and one-sided. Some of Iraq's surviving Type 69s were still in service during the second Gulf War in 2003, when they were used in a static artillery role. The T-54/55 was also used in the Balkan wars that accompanied the dissolution of the former Yugoslavia, and before that in Vietnam. The series was produced in at least 12 different versions, and was continually modified during its service life.

1948 France

AMX-13 LIGHT TANK

The AMX-13 was France's first postwar light tank design and was a huge success. It was exported to 24 countries, as well as being used by the French Army themselves.

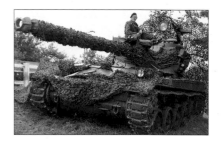

In the post-World War II years, the French Army urgently needed to re-arm themselves and drew up a requirement for three new armored fighting vehicles. One of these was a light tank, which was subsequently developed by Atelier de Construction d'Issy-les-Moulineaux under the name of AMX-13. The tank went into production in 1953 and proved to be one of the most successful vehicles of its kind ever to be manufactured. An estimated 7700 units were produced between 1945 and 1985, and about half of these were used for export. The 2.95in (75mm) gun of the original AMX-13 production model was modeled on the German L/71 Panther gun, and this was replaced by a 3.54in (90mm) weapon in 1966.

Geographical use

The AMX-13 was phased out of service with the French Army in the 1970s, but the vehicle was exported to 24 countries, and continues to be used by some of these. The biggest export customer was Singapore, which purchased 350 units. Some of the export variants are armed with a 4.13in (105mm) gun. The AMX-13 was used by the Israeli Army in the Six-Day War of 1967, but this version's 2.95in (75mm) gun was ineffective against the amor of the T-54 and T-55 main battle tanks used by Egypt and Syria, so the tank was phased out, with some being sent to Singapore.

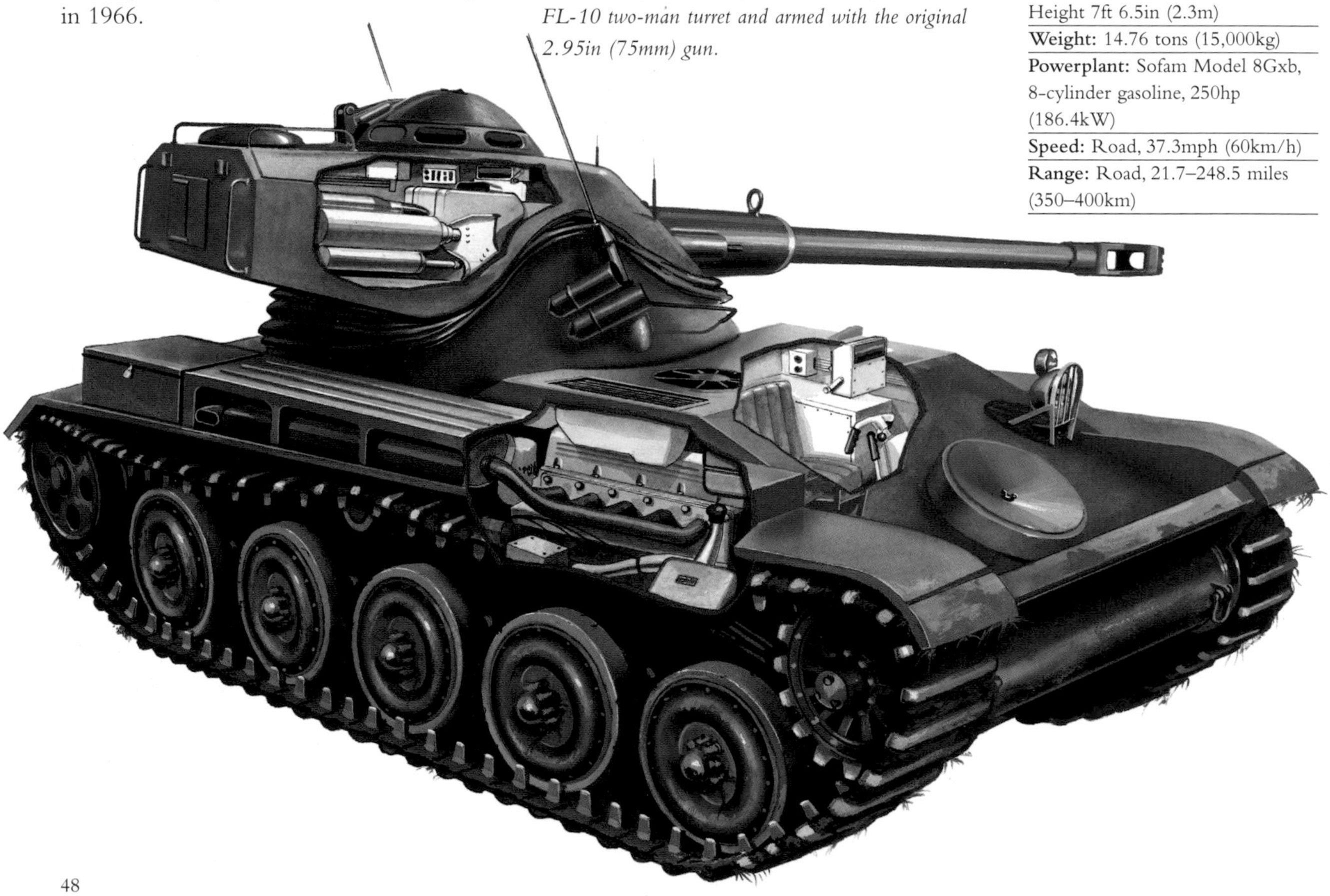

Below: *Diagram showing an AMX-13 fitted with an FL-10 two-man turret and armed with the original 2.95in (75mm) gun.*

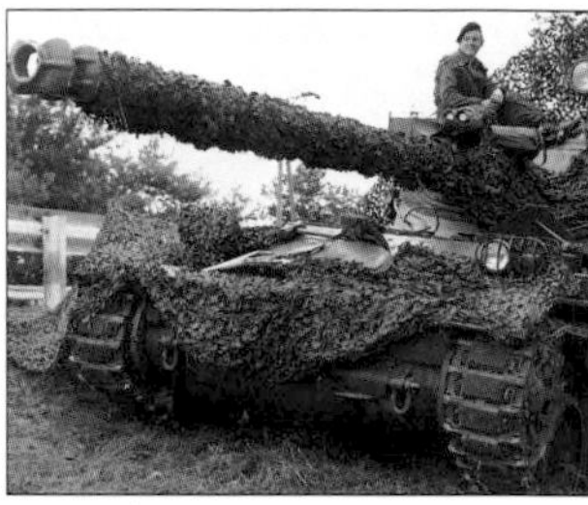

Above: *Later versions of the AMX were armed with a 3.54in (90mm) or 4.13in (105mm) gun, the latter pictured here.*

Specifications

Armament: One 2.95in (75mm), 3.54in (90mm), or 4.13in (105mm) gun; one or two 0.295in (7.5mm) or 0.30in (7.62mm) MGs
Armor: Maximum, 0.98in (25mm)
Crew: 3
Dimensions: Length, overall 16ft (4.88m); Width 8ft 2.8in (2.51m); Height 7ft 6.5in (2.3m)
Weight: 14.76 tons (15,000kg)
Powerplant: Sofam Model 8Gxb, 8-cylinder gasoline, 250hp (186.4kW)
Speed: Road, 37.3mph (60km/h)
Range: Road, 21.7–248.5 miles (350–400km)

Above: The PT-76 continues in use with armies that were once allied to the former Warsaw Pact.

PT-76 LIGHT AMPHIBIOUS TANK

Developed in the late 1940s, the Russian PT-76 has proved itself to be an excellent design. It is still in service in many parts of the world.

Specifications

Armament: One 3in (76.2mm) D056T gun; one 0.3in (7.62mm) SGMT MG; sometimes one 0.5in (12.7mm) DShKM antiaircraft MG

Armor: 0.197–0.67in (5–17mm)

Crew: 3

Dimensions: Length 22ft 8in (6.91m); Width 10ft 4in (3.14m); Height 7ft 5in (2.255m)

Weight: 13.78 tons (14,000kg)

Powerplant: One V-6 6-cylinder diesel, 240bhp (179kW) at 1800rpm

Speed: land 28mph (45km/h), water 6.2mph (10km/h)

Range: Road, 174 miles (280km); Water 40.4 miles (65km)

Development of the PT-76 light amphibious tank began in 1949, and the type was accepted for service in 1952. Production started in 1953 at the Stalingrad (later Volgograd) Tank Factory, and the vehicle was adopted as the standard reconnaissance tank of the Soviet and Warsaw Pact armed forces. PT-76 is an abbreviation of Plavayushchy Tank (literally "swimming tank").

About 7000 PT-76s were built before production ended in 1963; 2000 vehicles were exported to 24 countries under Soviet influence. This production total includes an improved variant, the PT-76B, which appeared in 1958. The type was also produced

Above: A PT-76 rolling ashore from a Soviet landing craft during an amphibious warfare exercise. The tank has seen a good deal of action around the world.

in China as the Type 63, and many of these were exported to Pakistan, Sudan, Tanzania, and Vietnam. India acquired large numbers of PT-76s, and these were used in the Indo-Pakistan wars of 1965 and 1971. The PT-76 has also been used in the Arab-Israeli wars, and in the counterinsurgency role in countries such as Indonesia.

Continued use

The PT-76 was still in widespread use in the early part of the 21st century.

⚔ 1953 USA

M48 MAIN BATTLE TANK

One of the most widely used medium tanks in the world, the M48 was a successful design from the outset, and went on to perform well in conflicts around the world.

The M47 had been in service for only a year when the US Army decided to replace it with another product of the Patton series, the M48. This had a new turret, redesigned hull and improved suspension. It entered production in 1952 at Chrysler's Delaware Tank Plant. The early versions of the M48 used gasoline engines, but combat experience in the Arab-Israeli war of 1956 showed that it readily burst into flames when hit, just as the early Shermans had done in World War II. In 1959, Chrysler upgraded existing tanks to produce the M48A3 model, which featured a diesel powerplant. Production of the M48 ended that year, by which time over 11,700 units had been built.

Upgrades

In the mid-1970s the M48 was upgraded and fitted with a 4.13in (105mm) gun, making it more compatible with the M60 (alongside which it operated). This variant was designated M48A5. By this time, most of the

Above: An M48 advances during street fighting in Saigon in May 1968. The M48 was intended for long-range engagements, and in Vietnam a gunner often had to be carried on the rear deck for close-in protection.

Specifications

(M48A5)

Armament: One 4.13in (105mm) L7 gun; three 0.3in (7.62mm) MGs

Armor: 7in (180mm)

Crew: 4

Dimensions: Length (over gun) 30ft 6in (9.31m); Width 11ft 11in (3.63m); Height 10ft 1in (3.01m)

Weight: 48.2 tons (48,987kg)

Powerplant: Continental AVDS-1790-2 12-cylinder supercharged diesel, 750hp (559.7kW)

Speed: 30mph (48km/h)

Range: 310 miles (499km)

Left: *Israel's M48s have 3.94-in (105mm) guns, diesel engines, and low-profile commander's cupolas. Many have been retrofitted with the same explosive reactive armor (ERA) fitted to the IDF's M60 tanks.*

Below: *US Marines ride ashore on an M48 during an exercise. The M48 was very effective in American hands, but less so in the service of other armies whose tactics left much to be desired. It was outfought by the British-built Centurion.*

M48s had been relegated to National Guard and Reserve formations, but it continued to be used by frontline formations, and the Americans allowed other operators them to upgrade their M48s to M48A5 standard. In Germany, the Federal German Army upgraded 650 M48s by replacing the US M68 41.3in (105mm) gun with the British L7A3 weapon and other equipment. In this guise it became known as designation M84A2GA2.

Combat

The M48 was used in combat during the Vietnam War, where it was used in an infantry support role. It was first used in tank-versus-tank combat during the Indo-Pakistan war of 1965, where it suffered heavy losses, particularly against the Indian Army's Centurions. At the Battle of Asal

Uttar, during an assault on Indian positions, the Pakistanis lost 100 M48s, although losses decreased after the Pakistanis revised their tactics. Poor tactics were largely responsible for the losses inflicted by Israeli M48s on Egyptian T-54s and T-55s in the Sinai desert during the Six-Day War of 1967, but on the West Bank, Jordanian M48s were outfought by Israeli M4 Shermans. Again, this was due to better Israeli tactics. Many Jordanian M48s were captured and put into Israeli service.

Continuing service

Many foreign countries are still using the M48 in the early part of the 21st century and it remains a viable fighting vehicle, although it is becoming increasingly vulnerable to portable antitank weapons.

⚒ 1956 USA

M113 ARMORED PERSONNEL CARRIER

Below: The Norwegian army's fleet of upgraded M113A1 vehicles are fitted with a Hägglands one-man turret armed with a Rheinmetall 20mm MK Rh 202 cannon.

The M113 is the world's most widely used armored personnel carrier. By 1992 production totaled 75,000 units, and further production runs have brought the figure to over 80,000.

Specifications

(M113A1)

Armament: Various, but minimum usually one 0.50in (12.7mm) MG

Armor: 1.77in (45mm)

Crew: 2 plus 11

Dimensions: Length 8ft 3in (2.52m); Width 8ft 10in (2.69m); Height (to hull top) 6ft 1in (1.85m)

Weight: 11.16 tons (11,343kg)

Powerplant: General Motors 6V53 6-cylinder diesel, 212hp (158.2kW)

Speed: 38mph (61km/h)

Range: 298 miles (480km)

With production exceeding 80,000 units, the M113 is the most widely used armored fighting vehicle of all time. Introduced in 1960, it was developed to transport airborne troops in transport aircraft like the Lockheed C-130 Hercules, as well as to perform its primary role as a battlefield APC. The original M113 model was powered by a gasoline engine, and this was replaced in 1964 by the diesel-powered M113A1. The M113A2 entered service in 1979. This was essentially the same model as the A1 but had an improved cooling system and suspension. It was followed by the M113A3, which was fitted with a more powerful turbocharged diesel engine. The M113 was only lightly armored: It was designed to provide protection from shrapnel for its 11 troops before they disembarked in the forward battle area.

ACAV version

More armor protection was added to produce an ACAV (Armored Cavalry) version, which was transformed into a true armored fighting vehicle by the addition of shields for its machine guns.

Above: The M113 has been used by 50 countries and has been produced in several versions to perform different tasks, such as that of command vehicle.

⚒ **1960   France**

PANHARD AML LIGHT ARMORED CAR

This excellent French armored car has been in continuous production for nearly half a century. It has been supplied to over 40 countries worldwide and used regularly in combat.

Specifications

Armament: One 3.54in (90mm) low-recoil gun; one 0.30in (7.62mm) MG

Armor: Maximum, 0.47in (12mm)

Crew: 3

Dimensions: Length, hull 12ft 5.2in (3.79m); Width 6ft 5.5in (1.97m); Height 6ft 9.5in (2.07m)

Weight: 5.41 tons (5500kg)

Powerplant: Panhard Model 4 HD, 4-cylinder gasoline, 90hp (67.2kW) or Peugeot XD 3T, 4-cylinder diesel, 98hp (73kW)

Speed: Road, 56mph (90km/h)

Range: Road, 373 miles (600km)

Left: The Panhard AML armored car has been one of the most successful wheeled armored fighting vehicles produced since the end of World War II, with over 4000 manufactured in France and South Africa.

The Panhard AML (Automitrailleuse Legère) was developed to meet a request to replace the Daimler Ferret, which had been used in large numbers. The AML prototypes were produced in 1959 and the first production vehicles were issued to the French light armored units in 1961. Since then, over 4800 units have been built both for the French Army and for export purposes. The armored car has been built in two versions, the AML 60 and AML 90—the latter being armed with a Hispano 3.54in (90mm) gun. The Eland 60 and Eland 90 are license-produced versions for the South African Army.

The Panhard AML has been used in Angola and the Falklands, where it was used by the Argentine forces, and in the Lebanese Civil War between 1975 and 1990. Its export to over 40 countries is some indication of its success.

Weapons

The AML 60 carries a number of weapons, including a 2.36in (60mm) breech-loading mortar and various machine-gun combinations. Some of the later vehicles are armed with a 0.79in (20mm) cannon.

Left: The Panhard AML has seen a good deal of action around the world, from the Falkland Islands (where it was used by Argentinian forces) to the Lebanon. It is used by over 40 countries.

⚒ 1960 USA

M60 MAIN BATTLE TANK

The M60 main battle tank was developed in the late 1950s to counter the threat from Russia's new T-62 medium tank. It did not meet the T-62 in combat for another 30 years, however.

The M60 was the last in the line of US main battle tanks that began with the M46. Its development began in response to intelligence in 1957. This suggested that the Russians were developing a new medium tank, the T-62, which was armed with a 4.53in (115mm) gun that would make it superior to the American M48. The simplest solution was to fit the existing M48 with a more powerful engine and the British 4.13in

(105mm) L7. With these improvements, the modified tank (originally designated the M68) went into production in 1959 and was deployed operationally in 1960. Renamed the M60, its production run eventually totalled 15,000 units. The first prototypes and

Below: The M60 is one of the world's most successful main battle tanks, and has seen service with some 20 armies since it was first deployed in 1960. It was used in large numbers during the 1991 Gulf War.

Specifications

M60A1

Armament: One M68 4.13in (105mm) gun; one 0.3in (7.62mm) MG; one 0.50in (12.7mm) MG

Armor: 5.63in (143mm)

Crew: 4

Dimensions: Length (over gun) 31ft (9.44m); Width 11ft 11in (3.63m); Height 10ft 8in (3.27m)

Weight: 51.8 tons (52,617kg)

Powerplant: Continental AVDS-1790-2A V-12 turbocharged diesel, 750hp (559.7kW)

Speed: 30mph (48km/h)

Range: 311 miles (500km)

early production machines were completed at the Chrysler Corporation's Delaware Defense Plant, but from 1960 onward, production switched to the Detroit Tank Plant, also operated by Chrysler (although later taken over by General Dynamics). Production ceased in 1987.

Upgrades

The M60 underwent various upgrades during its operational life. The first took place in 1963, when the M60A1 appeared with a larger and better designed turret, improved armor, and more efficient shock-absorbers. The next variant, the M60A2, featured a redesigned low-profile turret with a commander's machine-gun cupola on top, giving the commander a good view and field of fire while remaining protected. It was also armed with a 5.98in (152mm) caliber main gun similar to that of the M551 Sheridan, which was able to fire the Shillelagh gun-launched antitank missile as well as normal rounds. The M60A2 was abandoned after a relatively short time, and most units were rebuilt to the standard of the next variant, the

Above: The M60's main 4.13in (105mm) gun was fitted with a thermal sleeve, which was designed to prolong the useful life of the barrel before it needed to be changed. The tank was progressively upgraded during its service career.

M60A3. This incorporated a number of technological advances, such as a new rangefinder and ballistic computer and a turret stabilization system. All American M60s were upgraded to this standard.

Geographical use

The M60 was widely exported and was first used during the Arab–Israeli Yom Kippur War of October 1973, as well as in the invasion of the Lebanon in 1982. M60s operating with the US Marine Corps and the Royal Saudi Army were also used in Operation Desert Storm in 1991, where they led the attack on Iraqi forces in Kuwait and subsequently the drive to Kuwait City. It proved effective against all types of Iraqi armor—including the T-62, which it had been developed to counter many years earlier.

⚒ **1961 Germany**

MARDER I INFANTRY COMBAT VEHICLE

The Marder I was NATO's first infantry fighting vehicle. It combined the qualities of an armored personnel carrier with those of a light tank. It will be replaced by a lighter and cheaper AFV in due course.

Specifications

(Marder 1A3)

Armament: One 0.79in (20mm) cannon; one 0.30in (7.62mm) MG

Armor: Maximum, 1.18in (30mm)

Crew: 3 plus 6 or 7 troops

Dimensions: Length 22ft 6.8in (6.88m); Width 11ft 1in (3.38m); Height 9ft 10.7in (3.015m)

Weight: Combat, 32.97 tons (33,500kg)

Powerplant: MTU MB 833 Ea-500, 6-cylinder diesel, 447.4kW (600hp)

Speed: Road, 40.4mph (65km/h)

Range: Road, 310 miles (500km)

In the 1960s three German companies were asked to submit proposals for a new infantry combat vehicle—in the same family as the one including the Jagdpanzer Kanone and the Jagdpanzer Rakete. Many different prototypes were built and trialed, and the Bundeswehr adopted the Marder (Marten) Schützenpanzer Neu M-1966. Rheinstahl was selected as the prime contractor, with MaK of Kiel as the principal subcontractor. Both companies now form part of Rheinmetall Landsysteme. The Marder entered service with the Federal German Army in 1971, and was the first AFV of its type to be used by NATO. For the first time, infantry traveling in an armored personnel carrier were able to carry effective fire support, as the Marder was equipped with a two-man power-operated turret mounting a 0.79in (20mm) cannon and a 0.30in (7.62mm) machine gun. The latest version of the Marder is the Marder 1A5, and is equipped with very effective anti-mine protection features.

Delays

The introduction of the Marder I into service was delayed because priority was given to the production of the Jagdpanzer Kanone and the Jagdpanzer Rakete.

Below: The Marder was the first Mechanized Infantry Combat Vehicle to enter service in the West, and was one of NATO's most effective ICV's for many years.

1961 Soviet Union

BTR-60P ARMORED PERSONNEL CARRIER

The BTR-60P is one of the most widely used armored personnel carriers in the world, and is used in some unexpected places. American forces encountered it in Grenada in 1984.

BTR stands for Bronetransporter (Armored Transport). This series of armored personnel carriers was introduced into service with the Red Army in 1960 as a replacement for the BTR-152, which had revealed a number of shortcomings. The first BTR-60P to be issued to the Soviet motorized infantry divisions had an open roof, but the next variant, the BTR-60PA, had an armored roof, although this meant that vehicle's capacity was reduced from 14 to 12 men. The next model, the BTR-60PB, had a more refined sighting system for its gun. All versions of the series were fully amphibious and were propelled by a single water-jet mounted at the rear. The BTR-60P remained in production until 1976, when it was superseded by the BTR-70.

Geographical use

It was used in combat by Egyptian and Syrian forces during the Yom Kippur War of 1973, and by the Russians in the invasion of Afghanistan, where many were lost to antitank rockets used by the insurgents. The vehicle has been used in over 40 countries, including Cuba, during its intervention in Angola.

Below: *The BTR-60PA variant has a fully enclosed troop compartment and can carry a maximum of 16 troops, although its usual complement is 12. It is normally armed with a pintle-mounted 0.3in (7.62mm) machine gun.*

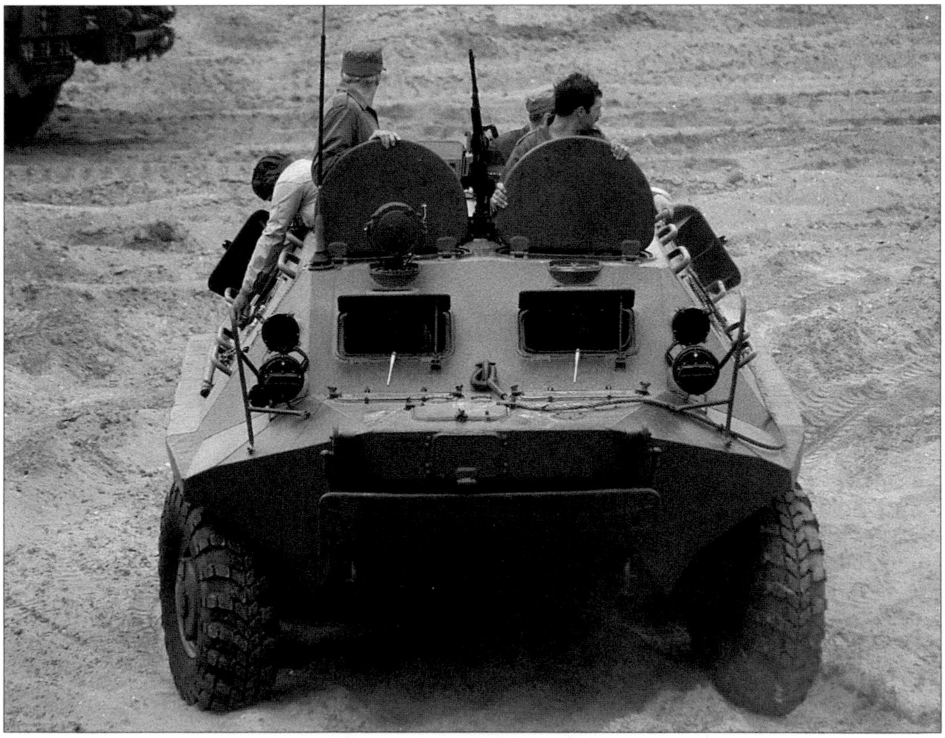

Specifications

BTR-60PB

Armament: One 0.57in (14.5mm) KPV MG; one coaxial 0.3in (7.62mm) PKT MG

Armor: 0.55in (14mm)

Crew: 2 plus 14

Dimensions: Length 24ft 10in (7.56m); Width 9ft 4in (2.85m); Height 7ft 7in (2.31m)

Weight: 10.1 tons (10,300kg)

Powerplant: Two GAZ-49B 6-cylinder gasoline, 90bhp (67.16kW) each at 3400rpm

Speed: land 50mph (80km/h); water 6.2mph (10km/h)

Range: 310 miles (500km)

1963 Germany

LEOPARD 1 MAIN BATTLE TANK

The Leopard 1 main battle tank was an extremely important element of NATO's landwarfare defense during the most dangerous years of the Cold War. It was originally intended to be a joint Franco–German collaborative project, but France withdrew and Federal Germany proceeded alone.

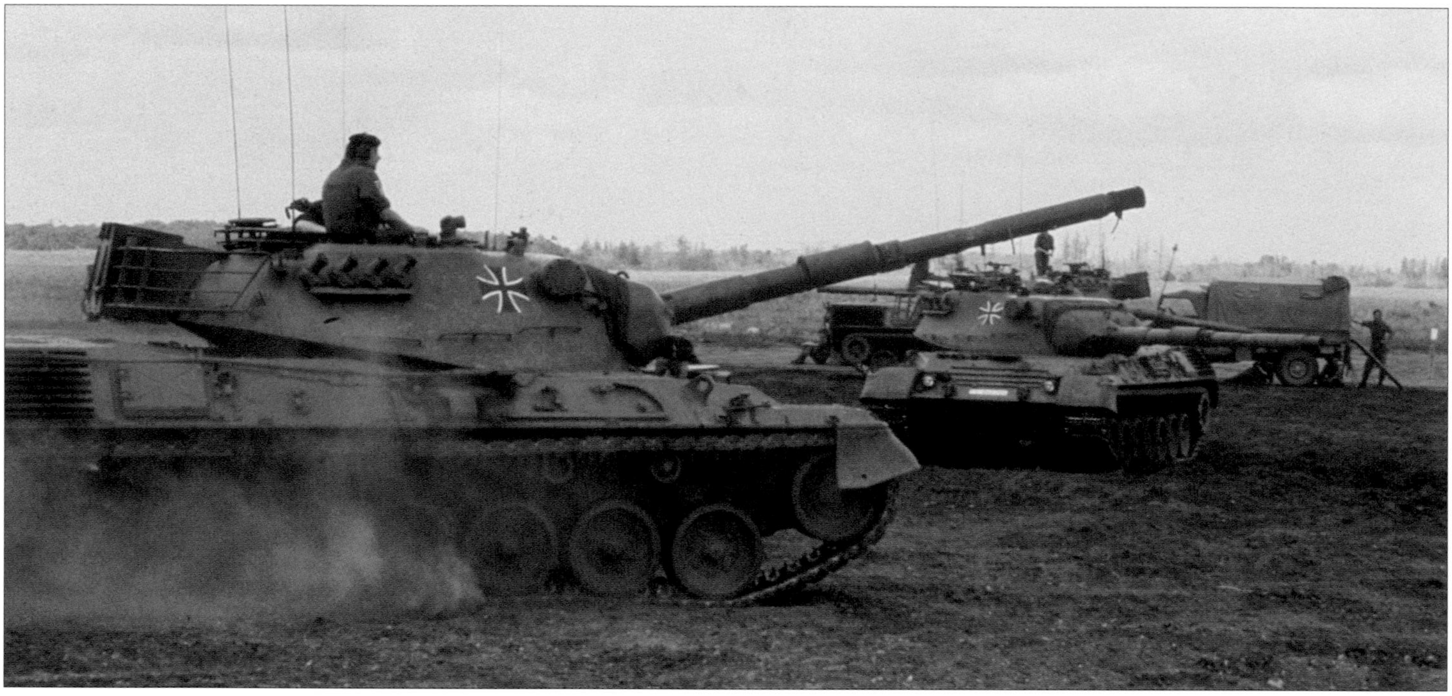

Above: *A Leopard Mk 1 during a training exercise in West Germany in 1984. The first production Leopard I was delivered to the Bundeswehr in 1965 and was produced in several versions.*

The Leopard project was initiated in 1956. Its aim was to develop a new AFV to replace the Bundeswehr's M47 and M48 tanks, which were becoming obsolete. The requirement called for a vehicle that would withstand hits from a 0.78in (20mm) antitank gun and be able to operate in an environment contaminated by nuclear, chemical, or biological warfare. The gun selected for its main armament was the British L7A3 4.13in (105mm) weapon. In June of 1957, Germany and France signed an agreement to develop the new tank. This was known initially as the Standard-Panzer. Two German and one French design teams were invited to submit proposals, each team producing two prototypes. Italy joined the development program in 1958.

Original design

Testing of the various prototypes began in 1960, and it was the design submitted by Porsche that was selected, although some changes to the original design were made before it was accepted for production. These included a new cast turret and several hull changes to raise the rear deck in order to make a roomier engine compartment. An optical rangefinder system was also added.

Upgrades

The first batch of production Leopard 1 tanks was built by Krauss-Maffei of Munich between September 1965 and June 1966. The next three batches comprised the Leopard 1A1 model, which included a new

Specifications

Armament: One 105mm (4.13in) L7A3 rifled gun; two 7.62mm (0.30in) MGs

Armour: Maximum, 70mm (2.75in)

Crew: 4

Dimensions: Length 9.543m (31ft 3.5in); Width 3.25m (10ft 8in); Height 2.61m (8ft 7in)

Weight: approx 40,400kg (39.76 tons)

Powerplant: MTU 10-cylinder diesel developing 619kW (830hp)

Speed: Road, 65km/h (40.4mph)

Range: Road, 600km (373miles)

Right: *When it was first produced, the Leopard 1 was a very capable main battle tank, offering a high level of agility and excellent firepower, thanks to its 4.2in (105mm) L7 gun of British design.*

Below: *The fact that the Leopard 1 is still operational with armies around the world in the early years of the 21st century is proof of the tank's excellent capability.*

gun stabilization system. The Leopard 1A1 was subjected to various upgrades in the 1970s. Follow-on models were the Leopard 1A2, with a more heavily armored turret; the 1A3, with a new welded turret; the 1A4, with a new computerized fire control system; the 1A5, with a completely new turret; and the 1A6, with additional armor and a 4.72 in (120mm) gun.

Exports

The Leopard 1 was exported to (or sometimes manufactured in) 12 countries. Italy was the biggest customer, acquiring 920 units. The other customers were Australia (90), Belgium (132), Brazil (240), Canada (114), Chile (unspecified), Denmark (330), Greece (335), the Netherlands (unspecified), Norway (172), and Turkey (307). The Bundeswehr employed 724 units, which were progressively replaced by the Leopard 2. During the Cold War, the Leopard and the British Chieftain would have borne the brunt of any tank battle that might have developed on the North German plain, and would have played a decisive part in blunting any Soviet offensive. The commonality between the armies using the Leopard in this sector—German, Belgian, and Dutch—would have been an important factor.

⚒ **1963 UK**

CHIEFTAIN MARK 5 MAIN BATTLE TANK

Until the introduction of the Leopard 2, the Chieftain was arguably the best main battle tank in service with any of the NATO forces during the 1960s and 1970s. It secured large export orders.

Specifications

Armament: One 4.72in (120mm) L11A5 gun; two 0.3in (7.62mm) MGs; one 0.5in (12.7mm) MG
Armor: Not available
Crew: 4
Dimensions: Length 24ft 8in (7.518m); Width 11ft 6in (3.50m); Height 9ft 6in (2.895m)
Weight: 54.13 tons (55,000kg)
Powerplant: Leyland L60 multi-fuel developing 750bhp (559.2kW) at 2100rpm
Speed: 30mph (48km/h)
Range: 248.5–280 miles (400–500km)

Left: *A British Chieftain main battle tank armed with a 4.72in (120mm) L11A5 rifled tank gun. The latter is fitted with a thermal sleeve to reduce barrel distortion and prolong its useful life before a change is needed. Several special-purpose variants of the Chieftain have been produced.*

The Chieftain, designed by Leyland, was intended to replace the Centurion as the main British battle tank, as the Centurion was becoming increasingly vulnerable to the latest generation of Soviet tanks and antitank weapons. The British decided to sacrifice lightness and mobility for effective armor protection, and to equip the new tank with a powerful 4.72in (120mm) rifled gun, which was very accurate. The prototype Chieftain appeared in 1959 and was followed by six more units, these being evaluated between 1961 and 1962.

Export

Nine hundred Chieftains were built for the British Army and the type attracted large export orders. Kuwait was an early customer, ordering 165 Chieftain Mk 5TKs. Twelve ex-British tanks were supplied to the Sultanate of Oman, who also took delivery of 15 new-build vehicles. The largest export order, however, came from Iran, who ordered 707 units in addition to a further 187 units of an upgraded model, the Improved Chieftain. The Iranian Chieftains were used in the Iran–Iraq war during the 1980s. Jordan also ordered 274 Chieftains. The Chieftain's one drawback was its engine, which was a multi-fuel type that never reached its planned power output.

Left: *The Chieftain is an extremely successful tank and attracted large export orders from countries in the Middle East.*

⚒ 1966 Sweden

STRIDSVAGN (STRV) 103 S-TANK

The Bofors Stridsvagn 103 S-Tank originated in a request by the Swedish Army to replace its fleet of 300 Centurions (among other armored fighting vehicles) with a homegrown product.

Specifications

Armament: One 4.13in (105mm) gun; three MGs

Armor: Not revealed

Crew: 3

Dimensions: Length 27ft 7in (8.42m); Width 11ft 10in (3.62m); Height 8ft 3in (2.50m)

Weight: 39.07 tons (39,700kg)

Powerplant: Rolls-Royce K60 multi-fuel, 240bhp (179kW) at 3750rpm and Boeing 553 gas turbine, 490bhp (365kW) at 38,000rpm

Speed: 31mph (50km/h)

Range: 242 miles (390km)

When the requirement for this tank was first issued, a heavy tank designated KRV was already under development. This was abandoned, however, and the emphasis switched to completing the Strv 103. The S-Tank tested a number of new design features, the most obvious of which was the absence of a turret. This layout was adopted so that the tank could keep a low profile in action, and this was further enhanced by its bulldozer blade, so that it could dig itself in if a static defense was required. The

disadvantage of a turretless design was that the entire vehicle had to be turned for aiming purposes. Although the tank could be slowed on its tracks as fast as a turret could be turned, this aspect was not attractive to potential customers. Although the design generated a high level of interest it did not attract any overseas customers. The S-Tank has a Rolls-Royce multi-fuel engine (later replaced by a Detroit diesel in the modernized Strv 103C) and a Boeing gas turbine.

Left: *This photograph shows the S-Tank's bulldozer blade in the retracted position. The last S-Tanks were withdrawn from service with the Swedish Army in 2001.*

Below: *The Stridsvagn 103 S-Tank was a bold design concept. The box at the rear of the hull is for external stowage of equipment. Novel though it was, the S-Tank did not attract overseas customers.*

⚒ **1972 Soviet Union**

T-72 MAIN BATTLE TANK

Fast and reliable, yet relatively cheap to construct, the T-72 was the first Russian main battle tank to be exported to countries outside the Warsaw Pact area.

The T-72 main battle tank entered production in 1972 and remained the principal Russian AFV until the collapse of the Soviet Union. First seen in public at a May Day parade in 1977, the T-72 was built under license in Czechoslovakia, India, Iran, Iraq, Poland, and the former Yugoslavia, where the tank was designated M-84. At least 50,000 of these vehicles have been built and the tank is in service with 30 armies around the world. The original version of the T-72 was the T-72A. This had a laser rangefinder and improved armor, while the T-72B had additional front-turret armor. The T-72BM

Specifications

Armament: One 4.92in (125mm) D-81TM (2A46M) smoothbore gun; one coaxial 0.30in (7.62mm) PKT MG; one 0.50in (12.7mm) NSVT AA MG

Armor: 9.84in (250mm)

Crew: 3

Dimensions: Length 31ft 3in (9.53m) (gun forward), 21ft 8in (6.67m) (hull); Width 12ft 9in (3.59m); Height 7ft 3in (2.22m)

Weight: 44.78 tons (45,500kg)

Powerplant: V-46 12-cylinder diesel, 780bhp (582kW) at 2000rpm

Speed: 40mph (65km/h)

Range: 250 miles (400km)

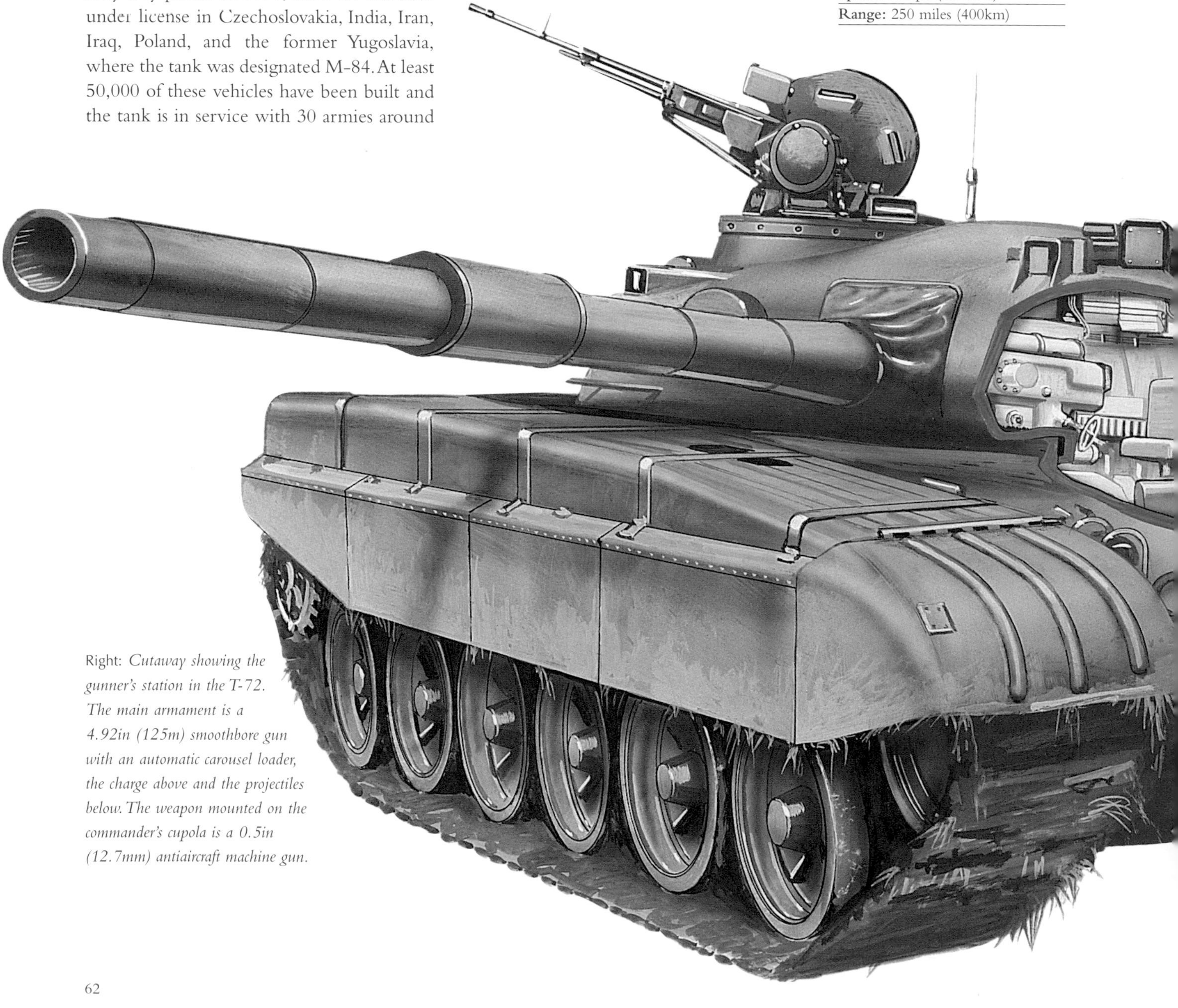

Right: *Cutaway showing the gunner's station in the T-72. The main armament is a 4.92in (125m) smoothbore gun with an automatic carousel loader, the charge above and the projectiles below. The weapon mounted on the commander's cupola is a 0.5in (12.7mm) antiaircraft machine gun.*

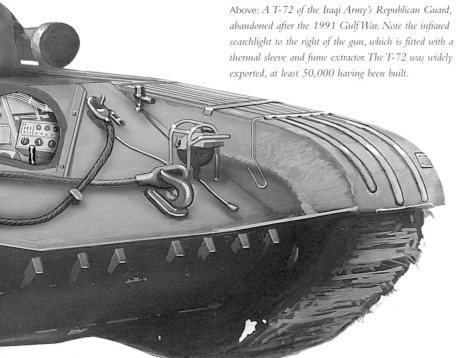

Above: *A T-72 of the Iraqi Army's Republican Guard, abandoned after the 1991 Gulf War. Note the infrared searchlight to the right of the gun, which is fitted with a thermal sleeve and fume extractor. The T-72 was widely exported, at least 50,000 having been built.*

was the first upgrade to incorporate Kontakt-5 explosive reactive armor; the export version of this is the T-72S. The T-72BK is a command vehicle with additional communications equipment.

Gulf War

The T-72 had the dubious distinction of fighting on both sides during the Gulf War of 1991. The Kuwaiti Army accepted the first of 200 tanks (the M-84 version) to be ordered from Yugoslavia. Iraq's Republican Guard is thought to have taken about 1000 T-72s, although these proved no match for the American M1 Abrams and the British Challenger.

RENAULT VAB ARMORED PERSONNEL CARRIER

The Renault VAB armored personnel carrier has been highly successful since 1976, and is used by many armed forces worldwide. It is an effective peacekeeping machine, and has been used in many trouble spots.

The VAB (Vehicule de l'Avant Blinde) frontline armored vehicle is an Infantry Corps tactical armored vehicle produced by the Euro Mobilite Division of Giat Industries, who have headquarters at Versailles in France. A joint venture company, Satory Military Vehicles, was set up by Giat and Renault Trucks with responsibility for the VAB series amongst others, including the AMX-10RC and the French Army's new VBCI wheeled infantry fighting vehicle. In September 2003, however, Giat was given the position of prime contractor as well as responsibility for marketing of the VBCI, the AMX 10P and AMX 10RC. Renault Trucks Defense, meanwhile, was the prime contractor for the VAB, and they also held marketing responsibilities. The first

production vehicles were completed at St. Chamond in 1976, and since then more than 5,000 VABs have been produced in 30 different versions. Large numbers of VABs were used in Operation Desert Storm, and this tank has been deployed in United Nations peacekeeping missions in Bosnia, Cambodia, Croatia, Lebanon, Rwanda, and Somalia. In addition to the 4000 VABs in service with the French Army, the AFV also serves with the armed forces of 15 other countries.

Below: *All versions of the VAB have a similar layout, with the driver front left, the commander/machine gunner on the right, the engine compartment to the rear of the driver, a small passageway on the right, and the troop compartment to the rear.*

Above: *This infantry combat version of the VAB features a turret armed with a 0.787in (20mm) cannon. The VAB was a major export success, having been sold to the armies of at least 16 countries.*

Specifications

Armament: One 0.50in (12.7mm) MG or one 0.30in (7.62mm) MG

Armor: Estimated, 0.98in (25mm)

Crew: 2 plus 10 troops

Dimensions: Length 19ft 7.4in (5.98m); Width 8ft 2in (2.49m); Height, hull top, 6ft 9in (2.06m)

Weight: 4x4 version 12.8 tons (13,000kg); 6x6 version 13.98 tons (14,200kg)

Powerplant: Renault MIDS 06.20.45, 6-cylinder diesel, 220hp (164kW)

Speed: Road, 57.1mph (92km/h); Water, 5mph (8km/h)

Range: Road, 621.4 miles (1000km)

1973   UK

SCORPION/SCIMITAR RECONNAISSANCE VEHICLES

Although the last Scorpion reconnaissance vehicles were withdrawn

in 1994, some of their chassis remained in use as the Sabre, which

mounted a 1.18in (30mm) cannon turret taken from other AFVs.

Manufactured by Alvis Vickers, the Scorpion light tank (or Combat Vehicle Reconnaissance Tracked Fire Support) was first used by the British Army in 1973. Designed to be a fast, air-transportable reconnaissance vehicle, it featured aluminum armor and mounted a 3in (76mm) L23A1 gun. The original model was fitted with a Jaguar 0.9 gallon (4.2 litre) gasoline engine, which had a very good power/weight ratio, although some models were fitted with the Perkins diesel engine. The Scorpion was an extremely compact AFV, and ideal for the reconnaissance role. The FV107 Scimitar was similar in appearance to the Scorpion, but mounted a 3.54in (30mm) Rarden cannon in place of

Above: *The original Scorpion was armed with a 3in (76mm) main gun, but this was later replaced by a 1.18in (30mm) Rarden cannon.*

the 3in (76mm) gun. Both the Scorpion and the Scimitar were used in the battle for the Falkland Islands in 1982, their light weight and tracks making it possible for them to cross the marshy Falklands terrain with ease. During the final assault on Port Stanley, they acted in support of 2 Para. The Scorpion was used by the British Army, the Royal Air Force Regiment, and 12 other countries. The largest user outside the UK was Belgium, who set up an assembly line for the production of 700 vehicles. The last Scorpions were withdrawn in 1994.

Specifications

Armament: One 3in/3.54in (76mm/90mm) gun; one 0.30in (7.62mm) MG

Armor: Not available

Crew: 3

Dimensions: Length 14ft 5in (4.38m); Width 7ft 2in (2.18m); Height 6ft 10in (2.09m)

Weight: 7.94 tons (8073kg)

Powerplant: Jaguar 0.9 gallon (4.2 litre) gasoline, 190bhp (141.6kW) at 4750rpm

Speed: 50mph or 45mph (80.5km/h or 72.5km/h)

Range: 644km or 756km (400 or 470 miles)

LEOPARD 2 MAIN BATTLE TANK

The Leopard 2 is an extremely powerful tank and is one of the finest of its generation, offering a unique blend of firepower, protection, and mobility. First delivered in 1978, it is still being radically upgraded.

As the successor to the Leopard 1, the Leopard 2 made its appearance in 1979 and is in service with the armies of Austria, Denmark, Germany, the Netherlands, Norway, Switzerland, Sweden, and Spain. Over 3200 units have been produced. The Finnish Army is buying 124 units and the Polish Army acquired 128 surplus Leopard 2A4 tanks from Germany. In August 2005, Greece placed an order for 183 surplus Leopard 2A4 and 150 Leopard 1A5 tanks from German Army reserves. In November 2005, an agreement was signed for the sale of 298 German Army Leopard 2A4 tanks to

Above: *The Leopard 2 has been procured by several nations, some of them obtaining licenses to manufacture the Leopard 2 locally.*

Specifications

(Leopard 2A5)

Armament: One 4.72in (120mm) smooth-bore gun; two 0.30in (7.62mm) MGs

Armor: Multilayer, thickness not released

Crew: 4

Dimensions: Length 32ft 8.4in (9.97m); Width 12ft 3.25in (3.74m); Height 8ft 7.9in (2.64m)

Weight: approx 58.75 tons (59,700kg)

Powerplant: MTU MB 873 Ka501, 12-cylinder diesel, 1500hp (1118.5kW)

Speed: Road, 44.75mph (72km/h)

Range: Road, 310 miles (500km)

Above: The Leopard 2 commander's low-profile cupola is on the right with the periscope sight to his front. The 4.72in (120mm) gun is fitted with a thermal sleeve and fume extractor, and the gunner's sight is immediately to the right of the mantlet.

Turkey, with deliveries planned over 2006 and 2007. The Leopard 2A6 includes a longer L55 gun, an auxiliary engine, improved mine protection, and an air conditioning system.

Upgrades

The 2A6 configuration has been developed for the German Army, and 225 2A5 tanks are being upgraded. The first of these was delivered in March 2001. A similar upgrade is also being carried out on behalf of the Royal Netherlands Army. The Leopard 2A6EX is a next-generation variant, 170 of which have been ordered by Greece. Other Leopard 2 customers are Spain and Sweden.

Left: The Leopard 2 relies for survival on its very advanced armor, which is of the spaced multilayer type and provides effective protection against most types of modern antitank weapon. Other vulnerable areas, such as the suspension, are protected by steel-reinforced rubber.

MOWAG PIRANHA ARMORED PERSONNEL CARRIERS

Specifications

Armament: Various

Armor: 0.39in (10mm)

Crew: 1 plus 13

Dimensions: Length 19ft 6in (5.97m); Width 8ft 2in (2.50m); Height 6ft 1in (1.85m)

Weight: 10.3 tons (10,500kg)

Powerplant: MOWAG V6 gasoline, 300bhp (223.9kW) at 2800rpm

Speed: 62mph (100km/h)

Range: 370 miles (600km)

The Piranha family of armored personnel carriers has proved a huge success for the Swiss MOWAG company. It has been manufactured in four countries and has attracted large exports.

Below: A variety of armament options is available for the Piranha, depending on the role for which the vehicle is intended, and can range from a single machine gun to a 4.13in (105mm) low-recoil gun mounted in a power-operated turret. The 8x8 version of the Piranha is used by the United States Marine Corps.

In the early 1970s the Swiss company MOWAG started developing a range of multiwheeled armored vehicles that had many common features and were able to undertake a wide variety of tasks. The first prototype of this family, subsequently called Piranha, was completed in 1972 and the first production vehicles came off the assembly lines in 1976. As well as being manufactured in Switzerland, production lines were opened in Canada (Diesel Division, General Motors of Canada), Chile (FAMAE), and the United Kingdom (Alvis Vehicles). All the UK-produced vehicles have been exported to Kuwait, Oman, and Saudi Arabia. The Piranha can undertake a number a roles, including those of ambulance, antitank armed with ATGWs, cargo, command, internal security, mortar carrier, recovery, reconnaissance, and radar carrier. The vehicles are fully amphibious, propelled through the water by two propellers at the rear of the hull.

Layout

All Piranhas have a similar layout, with the driver at front left, the Detroit diesel on the right, and a rear troop compartment with roof hatches and twin doors in the rear. The troop compartment has provision for firing ports and vision devices.

1979 Germany

TRANSPORTPANZER 1

The Transportpanzer 1 is still used in large numbers by the German armed forces. It carries out a wide variety of specialist roles in addition to its primary task of troop transport.

Specifications

Armament: One 0.79in (20mm) cannon or 0.30in (7.62mm) MG

Armor: Maximum, 0.39in (10mm)

Crew: 2 plus 10 troops (up to 14 on export models)

Dimensions: Length 22ft 4.9in (6.83m); Width 9ft 9.3in (2.98m); Height, hull, 7ft 6.5in (2.3m)

Weight: approx 18.7 tons (19,000kg)

Powerplant: Mercedes-Benz OM 402A, V-8 diesel, 320hp (238.6kW)

Speed: Road, 65.25mph (105km/h); Water, 6.5mph (10.5km/h)

Range: Road, 500 miles (800km)

The Transportpanzer 1 was one of a family of wheeled armored vehicles developed at the request of the Federal Germany Army in the mid-1960s. The intention was to develop vehicles with as many common features as possible. The 8x8 design emerged as the Spähpanzer Luchs (Lynx) (of which 408 units were built between 1975 and 1978), while the 6x6 design was developed into the Transportpanzer 1 armored personnel carrier by Rheinstahl (later to become Rheinmetall Landesysteme).

The company received orders for 1125 vehicles, the first of which was completed in 1979, and in 1983 10 units were delivered to Venezuela, which asked for them to be fitted with one 0.50in (12.5mm) and one 0.30in (7.62mm) machine gun. When used as an

Above: The Transportpanzer 1 has proved adaptable to a wide variety of roles. For example, the Spurpanzer Fuchs (Fox) is an NBC reconnaissance vehicle, while the TPz-1 Eloka is an electronic warfare version.

APC, the Transportpanzer 1 (TPz1) can carry 10 troops as well as its two-man crew, but there are a number of models with specialized roles.

Variants

The TPz 1A3/ABC Spurpanzer Fuchs (Fox), of which 140 vehicles were built, is a reconnaissance vehicle fitted with NBC detection equipment. There is also an engineer version, whose task is to transport mines and demolition equipment, an electronic warfare version, a command and control model, and an ambulance.

1980 Soviet Union

T-80 MAIN BATTLE TANK

Russia's T-80 main battle tank was used in Chechnya, where it proved vulnerable to rocket-propelled grenades. As a result, the latest model incorporates very sophisticated defenses.

Specifications

Armament: One 4.13in (105mm) gun; one 0.30in (7.62mm) MG; one 0.50in (12.7mm) MG

Armor: Steel; composite plates available

Crew. 4

Dimensions: Length 30ft 7in (9.33m); Width 11ft 1in (3.37m); Height 7ft 6in (2.29m)

Weight: 37.4 tons (38,000kg)

Powerplant: Model VR36 V-12 diesel, 730bhp (545kW)

Speed: 37mph (60km/h)

Range: 267 miles (430km)

Developed from the T-64, the Russian T-80 main battle tank first entered service in 1976 and was the first production tank in the world to be fitted with a gas turbine engine. The powerplant was developed by the Isotov design bureau and built by the Klimov factory, both of which had extensive experience in the design of gas turbines for helicopters. The engine provided more power than contemporary diesels, but it was fuel-hungry and the hull of the T-80 had to be redesigned to accommodate extra tankage.

Upgrades

Despite ongoing problems with the engine, and high manufacturing costs, the tank was ordered into production and subsequently underwent several upgrades, the first of which produced the T-80B in 1982. This was followed, in the mid-1980s, by the T-80U, which was equipped to fire the NK112 AT 8 Songster laser-beam-riding missile. The T-80U is fitted with new-generation Kontakt-5 armor and has an advanced fire control system incorporating an optical sight and laser rangefinder coupled with a stabilized image intensifier and active infrared sight. The latest version, the T-80UM-1 Bars (Snow Leopard) is fitted with very advanced antimissile equipment.

Below: *The T-80 pictured here is the T-80UK command tank version. It is fitted with laser detectors, aerosol mortars, and the Shtora-1 defensive system, of which its reactive armor forms an important part.*

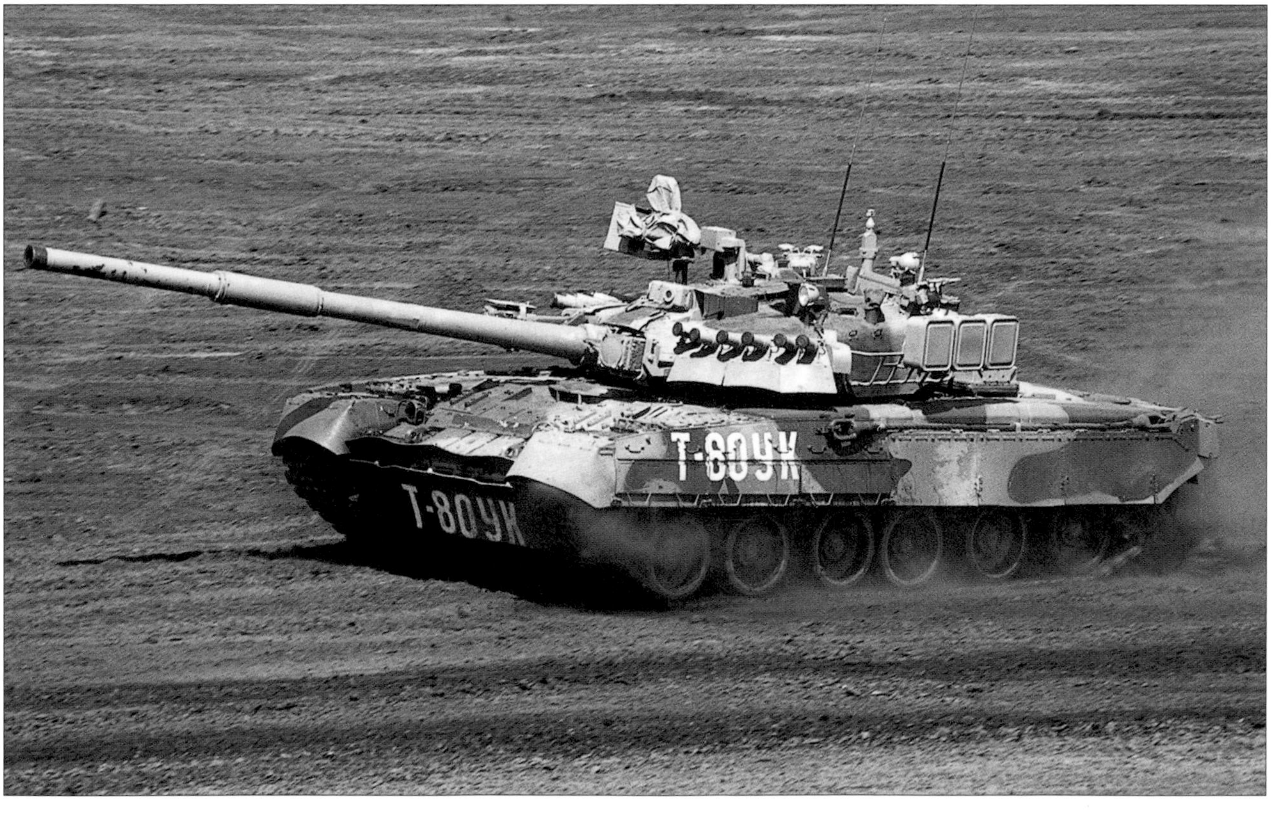

BV 206S ARMORED PERSONNEL CARRIER

Sweden has produced an excellent range of tracked armored fighting vehicles since the end of World War II. One recent example is the Bv 206S.

Right: *A Bv 206S at speed. The Bv 206 is unique among armored personnel carriers in that it consists of two units, connected by a steering unit. The vehicle is fully amphibious.*

Specifications

Armament: None

Armor: Not revealed

Crew: 4 plus 8

Dimensions: Length 22ft 7in (6.88m); Width 6ft 7in (2m); Height 6ft 3in (1.90m)

Weight: 6.89 tons (7000kg)

Powerplant: Steyr M16 direct-injected 6-cylinder in-line diesel, 186bhp (138.8kW) at 4300rpm

Speed: 31mph (50km/h)

Range: 230 miles (370km)

The Bv 206S is the armored personnel carrier version of the Hägglunds Bv 206 all-terrain vehicle, fitted with two all-welded steel bodies to protect the occupants from small-arms fire and shell splinters. The vehicle is used by the British and Swedish armies, and also by Finland. The vehicle consists of two all-welded steel units joined together by a steering mechanism. Steering is accomplished by two hydraulic cylinders, controlled from a conventional steering wheel. The front unit has accommodation for a driver and three passengers, while the rear unit has seating capacity for eight soldiers. The Bv 206S is fully amphibious, propelled in the water by its tracks. Each track assembly contains four pairs of roadwheels on trailing arms sprung by rubber tension springs. The track assemblies are attached to a control bar by two transverse leaf springs. The armor provides protection from 0.30in (7.62mm) ammunition and the

windows provide protection equal to the body. The British Army's use of the vehicle stems from a dual requirement for a tracked APC capable of operating in conditions of snow or of sand. The first production vehicles were delivered to the Swedish Army in 1981.

Below: *This convoy of Bv 206 APCs is seen in the environment for which the vehicle was intended, the snows of northern Sweden. The Bv 206 can be fitted with a roof-mounted Milan antitank missile unit.*

⚒ **1981 USA**

M2 BRADLEY

The M2 Bradley had a protracted development history and not all US Army chiefs were in favor of it, but it made a big impression in the Gulf War of 1991, destroying more Iraqi armor than the M1 Abrams tank.

The M2 Bradley was the culmination of a program initiated by the US Army in the early 1960s to develop a new Mechanized Infantry Combat Vehicle (MICV). This was to act as a supplement to, rather than a replacement for, the M113 armored personnel carrier. The first two prototypes of the new vehicle, the XM2, were completed by the FMC Corporation (later to become United Defense Ground Systems) in 1978. These were named the M2 Bradley Infantry Fighting Vehicle (IFV) and M3 Bradley Cavalry Fighting Vehicle (CFV). The former was designed to carry seven fully equipped troops, while the latter was intended for the reconnaissance and scout role.

Variants and upgrades

The M2 and M3 are similar in configuration. They are both equipped with an advanced two-person turret armed with an ATK Gun Systems Company stabilized 0.98in (25mm) M242 cannon and 0.30in (7.62mm)

Above: A Bradley Infantry Fighting Vehicle plunging at speed though the Iraqi desert. The Bradley underwent a substantial modernization program following the 1991 Gulf War, being fitted with appliqué armor among other refinements.

Right: *This photograph shows the commander and gunner of the Bradley in the central power-operated turret. This is the core of the vehicle's fighting capability, and is armed with a 0.98in (25mm) chain gun, a 0.3in (7.62mm) coaxial machine gun and a two-tube TOW missile launcher.*

Specifications

(M2A1)

Armament: One 0.98in (25mm) Bushmaster Chain Gun; one 0.3in (7.62mm) MG; two TOW missile launchers

Armor: Unknown thickness aluminum/steel

Crew: 3 plus 6

Dimensions: Length 21ft 6in (6.55m); Width 11ft 9in (3.61m); Height (turret roof) 8ft 5in (2.57m)

Weight: 22.58 tons (22,940kg)

Powerplant: Cummins VTA-903T turbocharged 8-cylinder diesel, 500hp (362.3kW)

Speed: 41mph (66km/h)

Range: 300 miles (483km)

Below: *Bradley IFVs traveling at speed through the desert. The Bradley confounded its critics by acquitting itself very well in the 1991 Gulf War.*

machine gun. The vehicles are also fitted with a twin launcher on the left side of the turret for a TOW antitank guided weapon. The first production Bradley AFVs were completed in 1981 and production continued up to 1995, with about 6800 units being built. Of these, 400 were supplied to Saudi Arabia, the only export customer. The latest models of the Bradley are fitted with explosive reactive armor, and automotive components of the vehicle are used as the basis for the Multiple Launch Rocket System (MLRS).

Improvements

Some of the improvements incorporated in the Bradley in recent years were a result of lessons learned in the Gulf War of 1991. The major improvements included an eye-safe laser rangefinder (ELRF), a tactical navigation system (TACNAV) incorporating the Precision Lightweight GPS Receiver (PLGR) and the Digital Compass System (DCS), a missile countermeasure device designed to defeat first-generation wire-guided missiles, and the Force XXI Battle Command Brigade and Below (FBCB2) Battlefield Command Information System. The internal stowage was further improved and a thermal-imaging system was added for the driver. During the Gulf War, M2 and M3 Bradleys destroyed more Iraqi armor than the M1 Abrams main battle tank. Twenty Bradleys were lost, three during combat and 17 due to friendly fire accidents. To remedy some problems that were identified as contributing factors in the friendly fire incidents, infrared identification panels and other marking measures were added to the Bradleys.

1983 USA

M1 ABRAMS MAIN BATTLE TANK

This tank will forever be remembered for its epic dash through the Iraqi desert during the Gulf War of 1991. It was used by the US armored divisions to cut off and destroy Saddam Hussein's Republican Guard.

Named after General Creighton Abrams (a former US Army Chief of Staff and commander of the 37th Tank Battalion), the M1 was designed by Chrysler Defense (later purchased by General Dynamics Land Systems Division). It replaced the M60 as the principal US Army and US Marine Corps main battle tank. The tank entered production in 1980 at the Lima Army Tank Plant, Ohio, and at the Detroit Arsenal Tank Plant, Michigan, before production became centralized at Lima.

Right: *Cutaway showing the interior and crew stations of the M1 Abrams. This excellent fighting vehicle had never been in combat before the 1991 Gulf War, but during that conflict it acquitted itself superbly, earning the unqualified praise of its crews.*

Features and use
The primary aim of the Abrams tank is to close with and destroy enemy forces using mobility, firepower, and shock effect. Three variants are currently being used, the M1, M1A1, and M1A2. The 4.72in (120mm) main gun on the M1A1 and M1A2, combined with the powerful 1,500hp (1119.4kW) turbine engine and special

Specifications

Armament: One 4.72in (120mm)
M256 gun; two 0.30in (7.62mm)
MGs; one 0.50in (12.7mm) MG

Armor: Unknown thickness
depleted uranium/steel

Crew: 4

Dimensions: Length (over gun)
32ft 3in (9.77m); Width 12ft
(3.66m); Height 8ft (2.44m)

Weight: 56.3 tons (57,154kg)

Powerplant: Textron Lycoming
AGT 1500 gas turbine, 1500hp
(1119.4kW)

Speed: 42mph (67km/h)

Range: 289 miles (465km)

armor (the equivalent of the British-designed Chobham) make the Abrams tank able to attack or defend large numbers of heavy armored forces. The Abrams performed very well during the 1991 Gulf War, dispelling concerns that it might not do so against the latest Russian equipment used by the Iraqis. In all, 1848 Abrams were deployed to the Gulf for Desert Storm, and in 2003 it returned to Iraq to participate in Operation Iraqi Freedom.

Production

Production of M1A1 tanks for the US Army is complete. Over 8800 M1 and M1A1 tanks have been produced for the US Army and Marine Corps, as well as for the armies of Egypt, Saudi Arabia, and Kuwait. The M1A1 is currently undergoing a modernization program, features of which include increased armor protection, suspension improvements, and a nuclear, biological, and chemical (NBC) protection system. The M1A1D modification consists of an M1A1 with integrated appliqué computer and a far-target-designation capability.

Right: The Abrams' main asset is its Rheinmetall 4.72in (120mm) smoothbore gun, one of the most powerful tank weapons in the world.

Above: *Thanks to its sophisticated fire control systems, the Abrams has an unprecedented first-shot kill power, as Iraq's Republican Guard—equipped with some of the latest Russian tanks—found to its cost.*

Upgrades

The M1A2 modernization program includes a commander's independent thermal viewer, an improved commander's weapon station, position navigation equipment, a distributed data and power architecture, an embedded diagnostic system, and improved fire control systems. The M1A2 System Enhancement Program (SEP) adds second-generation thermal sensors and a thermal-management system. The SEP includes upgrades to the processors and memory that enable the M1A2 to use common command and control software, which then enables the rapid transfer of digital situational data and overlays.

⚒ 1985 UK

WARRIOR INFANTRY COMBAT VEHICLE

Developed by GKN (now a part of BAE Systems Land and Armaments) the Warrior has proved itself to be an excellent fighting vehicle in different kinds of environment, ranging from the desert of Iraq to the mountains of Bosnia.

Below: *An excellent fighting vehicle, the Warrior distinguished itself in the 1991 Gulf War and has supported the British Army in its deployments ever since, proving well suited to terrain that has ranged from the Balkans to Afghanistan.*

Specifications

Armament: One 1.18in (30mm) Rarden cannon; 0.30in (7.62mm) chain gun

Armor: Not available

Crew: 3 plus 7

Dimensions: Length 20ft 10in (6.34m); Width 9ft 11in (3.00m); Height 9ft 2in (2.791m)

Weight: 24.11 tons (25,500kg)

Powerplant: Perkins diesel developing 550bhp (410kW) at 2300rpm

Speed: 47mph (75km/h)

Range: 410 miles at 37.3mph (660km at 60km/h)

The Warrior family of infantry fighting vehicles, of which there are seven variants, was first used in 1988 and subsequently proved to be a resounding success in the 1991 Gulf War, Bosnia, Kosovo, and for a second time in Iraq in 2003. One of the most impressive features of the vehicle is its powerful diesel engine, which gives it a road speed of 46mph (75kph) and allows it to keep pace with the Challenger 2 main battle tank over the most difficult terrain. The vehicle is not amphibious, but can wade up to a depth of 4.2ft (1.3m).

Armor

The infantry combat versions of the warrior are armed with a turret-mounted 1.18in (30 mm) Rarden Cannon, which will defeat most light armored vehicles out to 4921.26ft (1500m). The OPV and BCV variants have the turret, but with a "dummy" cannon to make space for artillery fire control equipment. All variants are equipped with a 0.30in (7.62mm) chain gun. The chain gun and the Rarden Cannon have a low-level air defense capability against helicopters. The gun is not stabilized and therefore engagement of point targets must normally be conducted from static, hull-down positions. The vehicle is fitted with an image intensifying (II) magnification RAVEN sight eight times, and there is capacity to store eight LAW light antitank missiles in the back compartment.

Above: This photograph depicts the repair and recovery version of the Warrior, seen in operation during Operation Desert Storm in 1991.

Protection and facilities

The Warrior's armor is designed to withstand an explosion from a 6.10in (155mm) shell at 32.8ft (10m) and direct fire from machine guns up to a caliber of 0.57in (14.5mm). During the first Gulf War and operations in the Balkans and Iraq, additional armor was fitted for protection. Collective CBRN protection is provided when closed down and the section can remain fully closed down for 48 hours. A toilet is also located in the vehicle.

Design features

Warrior section vehicles are able to carry and support seven fully equipped soldiers together with supplies and weapons for a 48-hour battlefield period in nuclear/biological/chemical conditions. The protection provided against small arms, missiles, and antitank mines was proven during the UN operations in Bosnia. Additional (appliqué) armor can be fitted. Thales Optronics STAG thermal-imaging sights are being added to upgrade the night fighting capability as part of the BGTI (Battle Group Thermal Imaging) program. To date, 1043 Warriors (of all variants) have been produced, some for service with the Army of Kuwait.

1986 France

LECLERC MAIN BATTLE TANK

France has produced one of the finest main battle tanks in the world in the Leclerc. The famous general whose name it bears would have been justifiably proud.

Built by Giat Industries, the Leclerc main battle tank was named after the famous commander of the French 2nd Armored Division and liberator of Paris in World War II. It became operational with the French Army in 1992 and with the armed forces of Abu Dhabi in 1996. An improved version, the Leclerc Mk 2, went into production in 1998; this has updated software and engine-control system. The French Army has 400 Leclercs in use, while the United Arab Emirates use 390 tanks and 46 armored recovery vehicles. The Leclerc is fitted with the FINDERS (Fast Information, Navigation, Decision, and Reporting System) battlefield management system, developed by Giat. FINDERS includes a color map display, which shows the positions of the host tank, allied and hostile forces, and designated targets. This can be used for route and mission planning.

Use by French Army

For many years the French Army had to rely on the ageing AMX-30 main battle tank as its principal armored spearhead. The introduction of the Leclerc, with its powerful 4.72in (120mm) gun and advanced fire control electronics, has given France's armored divisions new power.

Specifications

Armament: One 4.72in (120mm) gun; one 0.50in (12.7mm) MG; one 0.30in (7.62mm) MG

Armor: Not released

Crew: 3

Dimensions: Length overall, 32ft 4.5in (9.87m); Width 12ft 2in (3.71m); Height 8ft 3.6in (2.53m)

Weight: 55.61 tons (56,500kg)

Powerplant: SACM V8X-1500, 8-cylinder diesel, 1500hp (1118.5kW) or MTU 883, V-12 diesel, 1500hp (1119.4kW)

Speed: Road, 44.74mph (72km/h)

Range: Road, 279.5 miles (450km)

Left: *The Leclerc is well suited to desert warfare and has found an export customer in the United Arab Emirates, whose tanks have served on United Nations duty in Kosovo alongside their French counterparts.*

Below: *The Leclerc main battle tank a very effective fighting machine and incorporates all that is good in French tank design. Its 4.7in (120mm) main armament, coupled with a very advanced fire control system gives the French Army an armored capability that is second to none in the world today.*

1986 South Africa

LAND SYSTEMS OMC ROOIKAT ARMORED FIGHTING VEHICLE

The Land Systems OMC Rooikat has performed exceptionally well for the South African defense forces for over a quarter of a century. It has a complex and very effective fire control system.

Below: *Diagram illustrating the interior of the Land Systems OMC Rooikat (the name is Afrikaans for caracal, a large, long-eared, reddish-fawn cat). The vehicle can be armed with either a 2.99in (76mm) or 4.13in (105mm) main gun, supported by two 0.3in (7.62mm) machine guns.*

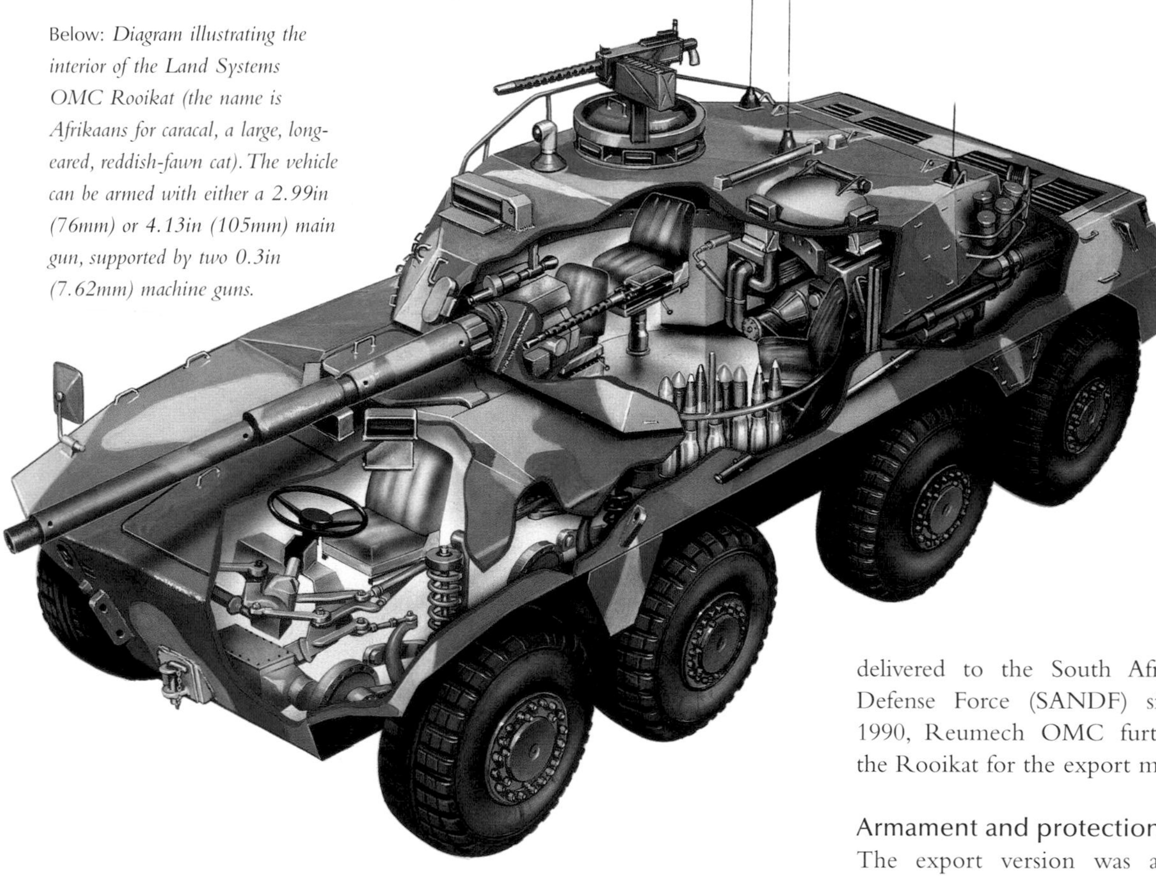

Specifications

Armament: One 4.13in (105mm) gun; two 0.30in (7.62mm) MGs
Armor: Classified
Crew: 4
Dimensions: Length 23ft 3in (7.1m); Width 9ft 6in (2.9m); Height 8ft 2in (2.5m)
Weight: 27.5 tons (28,000kg)
Powerplant: ADE V-10 diesel, 563bhp (420kW)
Speed: 75mph (120km/h)
Range: 622 miles (1000km)

The Rooikat armored fighting vehicle was originally developed by Reemit, which later became Vickers OMC. (This in turn was renamed Alvis OMC in 2002, following the acquisition of Vickers Defence by Alvis, and Alvis is now part of BAE Systems Land Systems.) The Rooikat is designed for fast day and night combat operations and is equipped with thermal imaging for night driving, navigation, and weapons deployment. Armed with a 2.99in (76mm) gun, 240 vehicles have been delivered to the South African National Defense Force (SANDF) since 1980. In 1990, Reumech OMC further developed the Rooikat for the export market.

Armament and protection

The export version was armed with a 4.13in (105mm) gun. The vehicle is equipped with two banks of 3.19in (81mm) smoke-grenade launchers, mounted in a forward firing position on each side of the turret. The system is electrically operated. The Rooikat is protected against the explosion of a T46 antitank mine, giving full protection to the four-man crew, and is also proof against hits by rounds of up to 0.94in (24mm) over its frontal arc. The vehicle can remain mobile following the loss of one wheel, thanks to its eight-wheel configuration.

⚒ 1988 Italy

ARIETE MAIN BATTLE TANK

The Ariete main battle tank is one of a family of three armored vehicles, which also includes the Centauro tank destroyer and the Dardo infantry fighting vehicle. The Italian Army has 200 of these tanks in service.

The Ariete (Battering Ram) main battle tank was the product of a consortium formed in 1984 by Otobreda and Iveco specifically to develop a new family of armored fighting vehicles for the Italian Army. First deliveries of the Ariete were made in December 1995, the last examples of the 200 on order being issued in 2002.

Design features

The Ariete has an all-steel welded construction, with composite armor on the hull front and turret front and sides, and side-skirts protecting the top of the tracks. The tank also has a laser-warning sensor mounted just ahead of the loader's hatch. The turret is in the center of the hull, with the commander and gunner on the right and the loader on the left. The commander has eight periscopes for all-round observation, while the loader has a single-piece hatch with two periscopes looking forward and to the left. The commander has a primary day and night (image intensification) stabilized panoramic sight (with magnification of x2.5 and x10). The gunner has a stabilized panoramic day and night (thermal) sight with laser rangefinder (of x5 magnification), which is linked to a ballistic computer, sensors, and muzzle reference system.

Specifications

Armament: One 4.72in (120mm) gun; two 0.30in (7.62mm) MGs

Armor: Not revealed

Crew: 4

Dimensions: Length (hull) 24ft 11in (7.59m); Width 11ft 10in (3.601m); Height 8ft 2in (2.5m)

Weight: 53 tons (54,000kg)

Powerplant: IVECO V12 MTCA turbocharged intercooled 12-cylinder diesel, 1300bhp (970kW) at 2300rpm

Speed: 40mph (65km/h)

Range: 342 miles (550km)

Left: *The Ariete has additional protection in the form of advanced armor over the frontal arc, offering protection against the latest high-explosive antitank (HEAT) warheads. The tank has a comprehensive suite of protective measures.*

Below: *The Ariete has four smoke grenade launchers on either side of the turret. The grenades can be automatically discharged when a laser warning system detects a threat. The system's sensor is mounted just in front of the loader's hatch.*

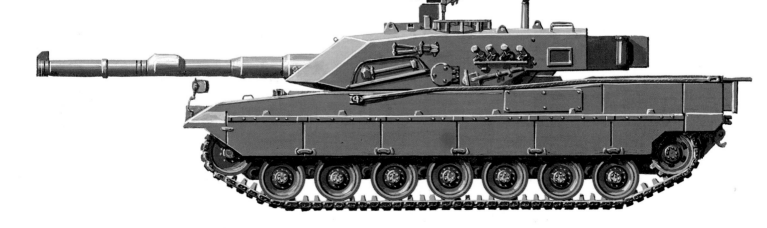

⚒ **1989 Germany**

WIESEL SERIES

The Wiesel series of light armored fighting vehicles was designed to be air-portable. As well as the versions already in production, trials are ongoing with new variants.

Specifications

(Wiesel 1 TOW carrier)

Armament: One TOW antitank missile launcher plus seven missiles

Armor: Not released, estimated 0.39in (10mm)

Crew: 2

Dimensions: Length 10ft 10.3in (3.31m); Width 5ft 11.9in (1.827m); Height 6ft 2.7in (1.897m)

Weight: 2.75 tons (2800kg)

Powerplant: VW, 5-cylinder diesel, 86hp (64.1kW)

Speed: Road, 46.6mph (75km/h)

Range: Not recorded

The Wiesel AFV was developed by Porsche in response to a Bundeswehr request for a light, air-portable armored vehicle. Production was taken over by MaK (now part of Rheinmetall Landsysteme), which delivered the first of 345 vehicles to the German Army in 1989. Of these, 210 would be equipped with TOW antitank guided weapons and 135 with 0.79in (20mm) cannon. The Wiesel 1 can be adapted to a wide range of other roles, including command and control vehicles, battlefield surveillance vehicles with radar, recovery vehicles, air defense vehicles carrying the Bofors RBS-70 SAM system, and tank destroyers armed with HOT antitank missiles.

Wiesel 2

Further development by MaK, as a private venture, resulted in the Wiesel 2, the first prototype of which was completed in 1994. The Wiesel 2 is larger than the Wiesel 1 with an additional roadwheel station on either side, a higher hull, a more powerful engine, and more internal volume. It is therefore able to undertake a wider range of battlefield roles. At one time it thought that the Wiesel was light enough to be air-dropped, but trials (which destroyed four test vehicles) soon revealed that it was not.

Below: *This Wiesel is equipped with a TOW optically tracked, wire-guided missile system.*

✹ 1990   Soviet Union

BMP-3 INFANTRY COMBAT VEHICLE

The BMP-3 is very well armed. Its turret mounts a 3.94in (100mm) gun and 0.30in (7.62mm) machine gun. The main gun has a supply of 40 rounds, including 22 stacked in an automatic loader.

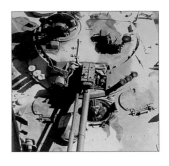

Above: *Bird's-eye view of the BMP-3's turret, showing the centrally positioned driver's station with hatches for additional crew to left and right. Note the grenade launchers mounted on the side of the turret.*

Developed by the Kurgan Machine Construction Plant, the BMP-3 infantry combat vehicle entered production in 1989. It is in service with the Russian Army, who had reportedly intended to replace the older BMP-2 with the new vehicle on a one-for-one basis. Lack of funds mean that the eventual total delivered was much less. Despite this, the vehicle has been a resounding success; over 600 have been exported to a number of countries, including the United Arab Emirates, Cyprus, Kuwait, and South Korea.

Variants

The BMP-3 is a tracked, armored, amphibious vehicle designed to engage armored ground and air targets while stationary, on the move and afloat. The BMP-3K is a command version (the same as the basic BMP-3) but it has additional communications and navigation equipment. The BMP-3F is designed for more sustained amphibious operations. It is able to remain at sea for seven hours and fire accurately in relatively high sea states. A reconnaissance version, the BRM-3K, is in use by the Russian Army.

Below: *The BMP-3 is probably the best-armed infantry combat vehicle in the world, its main armament comprising a hefty 3.94in (100mm) rifled gun backed up by a 1.18in (30mm) automatic cannon and a 0.30in (7.62mm) machine gun.*

Specifications

Armament: One 3.94in (100mm) 2A70 rifled gun; one 1.18in (30mm) 2A72 automatic cannon; one 0.30in (7.62mm) PKT MG

Armor: Unknown

Crew: 3 plus 7

Dimensions: Length 23ft 7in (7.2m); Width 10ft 7in (3.23m); Height 7ft 7in (2.3m)

Weight: 18.4 tons (18,700kg)

Powerplant: One UTD-29 6-cylinder diesel, 500bhp (373kW)

Speed: 43mph (70km/h)

Range: 373 km (600km)

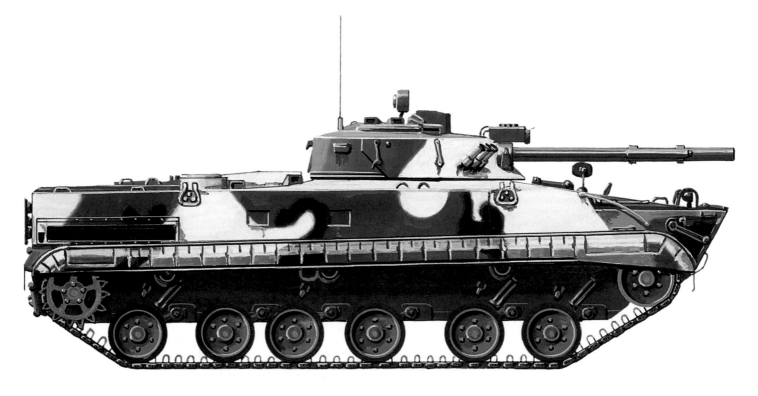

1992 Germany/Netherlands

FENNEK SCOUT CAR

The Fennek scout car was jointly developed by Germany and the Netherlands. It is a light and versatile vehicle that can be adapted to undertake a variety of roles. The name Fennek means "Desert Fox."

Right: *The Fennek is perhaps better described as a multipurpose carrier, as it is readily adaptable to a variety of roles. The interior can be configured to carry troops, supplies, or electronic equipment, and a small gun turret can be installed, as seen here.*

Specifications

Armament: One 1.57in (40mm) grenade-launcher or one 0.50in (12.7mm) MG, or one 0.30in (7.62mm) MG
Armor: Not revealed
Crew: 3 plus 5
Dimensions: Length 15ft 9in (4.8m); Width 8ft 3in (2.5m); Height 5ft 7in (1.7m)
Weight: 7.87 tons (8000kg)
Powerplant: DAF 6-cylinder turbocharged diesel, 210bhp (156.7kW)
Speed: 68mph (110km/h)
Range: 435–620 miles (700–1000km)

Originally known as the Multi-Purpose Carrier (MPC), the Fennek is a versatile light armored vehicle, in which modular design concepts have been fully exploited to make the vehicle adaptable. The vehicle is an international venture between Germany and the Netherlands. In 2006, 410 vehicles had been ordered by the German Army and 210 by the Dutch. Production is undertaken by the ARGE Fennek consortium, comprising SP of the Netherlands and Krauss Maffei Wegmann of Germany.

Design features

Fennek deliveries were scheduled to be completed in 2007. The tank has an all-welded aluminum armored hull, and the interior can be adapted considerably. Possible combat roles encompass those of battlefield reconnaissance and surveillance, command and communications, antitank missile carrier, supply vehicle, and combat engineer reconnaissance. For the antitank role, missiles can be launched from the roof of the vehicle, via remote weapon stations or manually from hatches, or alternatively from dismounted launchers at a distance from the carrier vehicle. The Fennek carries a sensor pod on a telescopic mast, enabling the crew to survey the surrounding area from an undercover position.

⚔ 1992 UK

CHALLENGER 2 MAIN BATTLE TANK

The British Challenger 2 is arguably the finest main battle tank in service anywhere in the world today. Its design has the benefit of experience from the Challenger 1 in the Gulf War of 1991.

Challenger 2 is the new-generation main battle tank in service both with the British Army and the Royal Army of Oman. It is developed from Challenger 1, which proved very successful during the Gulf War despite a number of shortcomings, such as a poor fire control system that resulted in a slow rate of fire. The Challenger 2 is fitted with a completely new turret and is protected by advanced armor technology. The Challenger 2 entered service with the British Army in June 1998, and the first vehicles were issued to the Royal Scots Dragoon Guards. This tank has been used in operational service in Bosnia and Kosovo, and British Army Challenger 2 tanks were deployed on active service in Operation Iraqi Freedom in 2003.

Below: *Although the Challenger 2 closely resembles its predecessor, Challenger 1, it is essentially a new tank, 150 improvements having been made to the hull alone.*

Specifications

Armament: One 4.72in (120mm) L30A1 gun; three 0.30in (7.62mm) MGs

Armor: Not available

Crew: 4

Dimensions: Length 27ft 4in (8.327m); Width 11ft 6in (3.52m); Height 8ft 2in (2.49m)

Weight: 61.51 tons (62,500kg)

Powerplant: Perkins Engines (Shrewsbury) CV-12 TCA Condor V-12 12-cylinder 26.1 litre diesel developing 1200bhp (894.8kW) at 2300rpm

Speed: 37mph (60km/h)

Range: 280 miles (450km)

Export

The Challenger 2 is built by BAE Systems Land Systems (formerly Vickers Defence Systems, then Alvis Vickers Ltd). The UK placed orders for 127 Challenger 2 tanks in 1991 and an additional 259 in 1994, the last being delivered in April 2002. In 1993 Oman ordered 18 Challenger 2 tanks, and an order for a further 20 tanks was placed in November 1997. Deliveries for Oman were completed in 2001.

Design features

The totally integrated fire control system provides both the commander and gunner with an independently gyrostabilized, optical/thermal sights, equipped with a laser rangefinder. The gunner's sight has limited traverse, whilst the commander's is fully panoramic. The tank incorporates second-generation TOGS thermal imaging. Its fire control system enables it to consistently engage and destroy multiple targets using its new high pressure 4.72in (120mm) L30 gun. To make full use of its formidable and accurate firepower, the Challenger 2 is designed to optimize the crew's operational

Above: A Challenger 2 at speed. The Challenger 2 underwent an extremely demanding series of trials before being accepted for service—the most demanding ever set, according to the UK Ministry of Defence. The Challenger 2E is an export version.

environment. Levels of noise and vibration at crew stations are minimized, fresh filtered air maintains a workable environment, and the layout and operation of systems and controls maximizes the crew's ability to achieve first-round hits under all conditions.

Armament and protection

Stealth is designed into the tank's construction to reduce the probability of detection on the battlefield by visual, electronic, and thermal means. All explosive material is stowed below the turret ring in armored charge bins and a nuclear, biological, and chemical (NBC) filtration system provides collective protection against ingress and maintains a positive vehicle internal pressure. The advanced armor technology resisted penetration during prolonged trials with a wide range of modern antitank ordnance.

1993 Soviet Union

T-90 MAIN BATTLE TANK

Russia's T-90 main battle tank is the latest development of the T-72 line, and is used in substantial numbers. It has also been purchased by India, who have made further modifications.

Specifications

Armament: One 4.92in (125mm) 2A46M Rapira 3 smoothbore gun; one coaxial 0.30in (7.62mm) PKT MG; one 0.50in (12.7mm) NSVT AA MG
Armor: Unknown
Crew: 3
Dimensions: Length (hull) 22ft 6in (6.86m); Width 11ft 1in (3.37m); Height 7ft 4in (2.23m)
Weight: 45.76 tons (46,500kg)
Powerplant: V-84MS 12-cylinder multi-fuel diesel, 840bhp (627kW) at 2000rpm
Speed: 40mph (65km/h)
Range: 400 miles (650km)

The T-90 main battle tank is the most modern tank owned by the Russian Army, and is a further development of the T-72. The tank entered production in 1993 and incorporates some subsystems of the T-80. It also features the latest development of the Kontakt-5 explosive reactive armor, which provides protection against chemical and kinetic energy warheads. By the mid-1990s, over 100 T-90s were in service with armored units in the Russian Far Eastern Military District. In 1996 an upgraded model made its appearance, featuring a fully welded turret in place of the original T-90's cast turret. In 2006 there were 241 T-90s serving with the Russian Army's 5th Tank Division in the Siberian Military District. In 2001, India was faced with a shortfall in modern armor following the debacle of it indigenous Arjun MBT design and purchased 310 T-90S tanks from Russia. Some of these vehicles were delivered in kit form for local assembly.

Indian variant

India has developed an improved version of the T-90S, known as the Bhishma. The name means "He of the Terrible Oath," and belonged to a hero in Indian mythology.

Below: *Although the T-90 is marketed by the Russians as a new tank, it is in fact an upgrade of the well-tried T-72. The T-90 is protected by both conventional and explosive reactive armor.*

M1114 HUMVEE LIGHT UTILITY VEHICLE

The Humvee light utility vehicle has been used in massive numbers by the US armed forces in recent years. The provision of armor has been a necessity due to the losses suffered in action.

Above: *The Humvee mounts a machine gun, as seen in these vehicles on night patrol. The vehicle was first used in Operation Just Cause—the 1989 invasion of Panama.*

The M1114 Humvee owes its origin—and its name—to a US Army request in 1979, for a high mobility multipurpose wheeled vehicle (which became abbreviated to Humvee). The intention was to supplement and eventually replace the Jeep and other soft-skinned transport vehicles in US service. The US Government gave a development contract to AM General, an American heavy-vehicle manufacturer based at South Bend, Indiana and well known for its production of the civilian Hummer vehicle. The company began design work in July 1979, and just under a year later the first prototype, designated M998, was completed. After more prototypes were evaluated, the company received a US Army contract for the production of 55,000 units, to be delivered by 1985. The Humvee was first used in 1989 in Operation Just Cause, the US invasion of Panama. Over 10,000 vehicles were deployed in support of Operation Iraqi Freedom in 2003.

M1114

As the Humvee is unarmored, the losses created by small-arms fire and rocket-propelled grenades led to the development of an improved version, the M1114. This has a larger, more powerful engine with a turbocharger, air conditioning and a strengthened suspension. It also boasts a fully armored passenger area protected by hardened steel and bulletproof glass. This version now accounts for most of the Humvee production.

Below: *The M1114 Humvee features a vertical hull front with vertical louvers, flanked by headlamps.*

Specifications

Armament: One M60 0.30in (7.62mm) MG or one 0.50in (12.7mm) MG or one 1.57in (40mm) grenade launcher

Armor: Unknown thickness steel

Crew: 3–4

Dimensions: Length 16ft 3in (4.99m); Width 7ft 6in (2.3m); Height 6ft 2in (1.9m)

Weight: 5.4 tons (5489kg)

Powerplant: V-8 turbocharged fuel-injected diesel, 190hp (141.8kW)

Speed: 78mph (125km/h)

Range: 275 miles (443km)

✶ **1994 Austria**

PANDUR ARMORED PERSONNEL CARRIER

The Austrian Pandur can be fitted with a large number of sensory devices and weapons, and is fully amphibious, propelled by water jets. Its defensive features include engine and exhaust silencing.

Produced by Steyr-Daimler-Puch of Vienna, Austria, the Pandur 6x6 armored personnel carrier was developed as a private venture. The first prototypes appeared in 1985, and in 1994 the Austrian Army ordered 68 examples for use by Austrian forces on United Nations duty. The Pandur is also used by Kuwait, who accepted 70 vehicles, Belgium (54), and Slovenia (10). The vehicle is manufactured in small numbers in the United States by AV Technology International, a division of General Dynamics. The Pandur 8x8 is an improved version, combining many features of the 6x6 with new ones. It can be air-transported in a Lockheed Martin C-130 Hercules. The Pandur's driver sits at front left and the engine is to the right. The driver is provided with a single-piece hatch cover as well as three day periscopes, one of which can be replaced by a passive periscope for night missions. The vehicle is fitted with a two-stage synchronized distribution gear box for both road and cross-country use. Improved suspension will be fitted for optimum cross-country mobility.

Specifications

Armament: One 0.5in (12.7mm) M2 MG

Armour: Unknown

Crew: 2+8

Dimensions: Length 19ft (5.69m); Width 8ft 2in (2.5m); Height 6ft 10in (1.86m)

Weight: 13.28 tons (13,500kg)

Powerplant: Steyr WD 612.95 6-Cylinder Diesel, 260 bhp (194kW)

Speed: 62mph (100km/h)

Range: 435 miles (700km)

Above: A 6x6 Pandur completing a river crossing. Note the waterjet under the starboard side of the hull. The armored front gives protection against 0.50in (12.7mm) projectiles.

Below: *The Pandur can be fitted with a variety of sensor equipment, as seen here with its sensor head elevated. This example is also carrying two Euromissile UTM 800 launchers for HOT antitank missiles.*

⚒ **1996   International**

ASCOD INFANTRY FIGHTING VEHICLE

The ASCOD infantry fighting vehicle, also available as a light tank variant, is a joint effort by Austria and Spain to produce a mobile and effective fighting vehicle. It features the most up-to-date equipment.

Below: The ASCOD infantry fighting vehicle is offered with a variety of armament fits. Pictured here is the LT 105 light tank variant, which is armed with a 4.13in (105mm) gun. Customers also have the choice of two engines.

Specifications

Armament: One 4.13in (105mm) gun; two 0.30in (7.62mm) MGs

Armor: Classified

Crew: 4

Dimensions: Length 21ft 8in (6.61m); Width 10ft 4in (3.15m); Height 9ft 1in (2.76m)

Weight: 28.05 tons (28,500kg)

Powerplant: MTU 8V 183 TE22 diesel, 600bhp (447kW) at 2300rpm

Speed: 43mph (70km/h)

Range: 310 miles (500km)

The ASCOD (Austrian Spanish Cooperation Development) infantry fighting vehicle is the result of a collaborative venture between Austrian Steyr-Daimler-Puch and Spanish Santa Barbara SA. The first production order was placed by the Spanish Government, who ordered 146 units in 1996. The vehicle is named Pizarro by the Spanish Army. They have placed a follow-on order for another 170 vehicles, with deliveries to be completed by 2010. The Austrian Army has acquired 112 units; the Austrian vehicles are named Ulan. The AIFV model is armed with a 1.18in (30mm) Mauser MK 30-2 automatic cannon and a 0.30in (7.62mm) coaxial gun. The turret is gyrostabilized to permit accurate shooting when the vehicle is in motion. It has a computerized fire control system, night-vision equipment, and a laser-aiming device. The Austrian Ulan is powered by a 720bhp (536.90kW) MTU 8V 1999 diesel engine, while the Spanish Pizarro is fitted with a 600bhp (447.42kW) MTU 8V-183-TE22 diesel engine.

Variants

A light tank variant, the LT 105, is also on offer and is armed with a 4.13in (105mm) gun. Thailand is buying 15 units of this version of the tank. There are several other variants, including recovery vehicles and command vehicles.

⚒ **1998 Canada**

LAV III ARMORED FIGHTING VEHICLE

The LAV III armored fighting vehicle is in service with the US military and the Canadian and New Zealand armed forces. It has proved its worth many times over on United Nations peacekeeping operations.

Below: *The LAV III is a robust fighting vehicle. It is widely used by the Canadian Armed Forces and has seen operational service on United Nations deployments overseas.*

The LAV III is the latest derivative of the LAV light armored vehicle family. It is based on the Swiss Piranha which was originally developed for service for the United States Marine Corps. The Canadian Army is the largest operator of the LAV III, and uses the vehicle in a variety of roles, including as an infantry carrier, a command post, for forward observation, engineer variants, and TOW missile carriers. The LAV III was first used by the Canadian Army in 1999, and 651 vehicles have been delivered. The New Zealand Army has also accepted 105. The infantry carrier version is able to accommodate up to seven infantrymen and a crew of three (gunner, driver, and commander). In addition to the 0.98in (25mm) cannon, the LAV III turret also features a coaxial 0.30in (7.62mm) machine gun, a top-mounted 0.218in (5.56mm) or 0.30in (7.62mm) machine gun, and one 0.30in (76mm) grenade launcher. Canadian LAV IIIs have been used overseas during United Nations deployments with the Canadian armed forces.

The Stryker

In US military service, the LAV III is known as the Stryker, in honor of two unrelated soldiers of that name, one killed in World War II and the other in Vietnam.

Specifications

Armament: One 0.98in (25mm) cannon; one 0.30in (7.62mm) MG; one 0.218in (5.56mm) MG

Armor: Classified

Crew: 3 plus 8

Dimensions: Length 22ft 9in (6.934m); Width 8ft 9in (2.667m); Height 9ft 3in (2.82m)

Weight: 16.24 tons (16,500kg)

Powerplant: Caterpillar 3126 series diesel, 350bhp (261kW)

Speed: 62mph (100km/h)

Range: 310 miles (500km)

Specifications

Armament: One 4.92in (125mm) gun; one 0.30in (7.62mm) MG; one 0.50in (12.7mm) MG

Armor: Not available

Crew: 3

Dimensions: Not available

Weight: Not available

Powerplant: Not available

Speed: Not available

Range: Not available

⚒ 1998 China

TYPE 98 MAIN BATTLE TANK

Produced by Norinco, the Type 98 main battle tank has not performed well during its evaluation period with the Chinese Army. This has necessitated a series of modifications.

Below: The Type 98 has a high power-to-weight ratio and as a consequence is likely to be an agile vehicle with a high speed.

This tank was first shown to the public in October 1999, when it took part in a parade to mark the 50th anniversary of the People's Republic of China. It was in effect the prototype of the Chinese Army's third-generation main battle tank. Four prototypes of the original Type 98 design were tested between 1995 and 1996. It is an updated and improved version of the Type 90, which is a derivative of the T-72 developed for export. The Type 98 comprises a T-72 chassis. This is surmounted by a new two-man turret armed with a 4.92in (125mm) smoothbore gun fed by an automatic loader.

Above: A Type 98 squats menacingly in the snow.

Type 98

The Type 98 was produced in limited numbers and gave way to the Type 98G, which has a modified turret and is now designated Type 99. The Type 99 possesses an advanced computer-based fire control system that enables it to engage targets on the move. Its 4.92in (125mm) main armament can fire a laser-guided projectile. The tank has a high power–weight ratio and possesses a high performance and considerable agility.

2002 Italy

DARDO INFANTRY FIGHTING VEHICLE

This tank was developed by the Consorzio Iveco Oto to meet a need of the Italian Army for a modern vehicle to carry out UN peacekeeping and security operations. The Dardo was previously called the VCC-80 IV.

Specifications

Armament: 0.98in (25mm) cannon; 0.3in (7.62mm) coaxial machine gun

Armor: All-welded aluminum with ballistic steel on hull and turret

Crew: 2 plus 7

Dimensions: Length 22 ft (6.71m); Width 9ft 10in (3m); Height 8ft 8in (2.64 m)

Weight: 22.64 tons (23,000kg)

Powerplant: IVECO 8260 liquid-cooled V-6 diesel, 520hp (388 kW)

Speed: 43.5 mph (70 km/h)

Range: 311 miles (500 km)

Above: *The Dardo Infantry Fighting Vehicle can carry its own antitank capability in the form of two single-tube TOW missile launchers mounted on the turret. The TOW missile is effective up to 3750 yards (3430m).*

The Dardo is an infantry fighting vehicle designed to operate together with MBTs and provide a soldier squad with adequate protection, fast deployment, and fire support. In 1999, the Italian Army ordered 200 Dardo vehicles in basic configuration, armed with an Oto Melara 0.98in (25mm) HITFIST turret, plus four vehicles in special versions (command and control, ambulance, mortar carrier, and antitank). The first Dardo was delivered in May 2002. By adopting this vehicle, the Italian Army is now equipped with a modern system. It is also effective in peacekeeping missions thanks to its high protection (the hull and turret are made of all-welded aluminum with outer plates of high hardness steel), mobility (the Iveco engine and the automatic transmission allow the Dardo to achieve a speed exceeding 19.44mph [70 km/h] on the road) and the capacity to perform surgical firing actions with its TOW missiles. The Italian Army is considering the acquisition of another batch of several hundred vehicles, including special versions.

Below: *This shows the large rear ramp through which the infantry enter and leave the vehicle. The ramp is power-operated, although it incorporates a manually operated door for emergency use.*

⚒ **2007 Germany**

BOXER

The Boxer multi-role armored vehicle began as a joint venture between the UK, Germany, and the Netherlands, but the UK pulled out of the program in 2003.

Specifications

Armament: Reconfigurable to suit operations and national requirements

Armor: Unknown

Crew: Up to 11

Dimensions: Length 25ft 7in (7.88m); Width 11ft 10in (3.61m); Height 9ft 9in (2.99m)

Weight: 25.2 tons (25,604kg)

Powerplant: 711hp (530kW)

Speed: 64 mph (103 km/h)

Range: 652m (1050 km)

Left: *The Boxer design makes provision for an 8x8 armored personnel carrier (pictured here) and command vehicle versions, and also allows for the development of other variants using the same base vehicle.*

In November 1999, the governments of the UK and Germany signed a contract for the collaborative development and initial production of the family of next-generation armored utility vehicles. The program was known as the Multi-Role Armoured Vehicle (MRAV) in the UK, and the Gepanzertes Transport-Kraftfahrzeug (GTK) in Germany. In February 2001, the Netherlands signed a Memorandum of Understanding to join the program. The Dutch program is called the Pantser Wiel Voertuig (PWV). In December 2002, it was announced that the vehicle would be called the Boxer. An industrial group, ARTEC GmbH (consisting of Krauss-Maffei Wegmann [KMW] and Rheinmetall Landsysteme from Germany, and Stork of the Netherlands) is the prime contractor for the program. The UK withdrew from the program in 2003 but the other two nations went ahead.

Prototypes and production

The first prototype, in German APC configuration, was completed in December 2002 and the first Dutch prototype, a Command Post version, was completed in October 2003. Germany has ordered 1000 vehicles and the Netherlands have ordered 384. The Boxer will replace M113 and Fuchs Tpz 1 vehicles in the Germany Army, and YPR and M577 vehicles in the Royal Netherlands Army.

Left: *In July 2003, the UK Ministry of Defence announced that it would withdraw from the program to pursue a new national program, the Future Rapid Effect System (FRES). The MoD requires a lighter more easily deployable vehicle.*

INDEX